# Algebra Activities from Many Cultures

Beatrice Lumpkin

J. WESTON
WALCH
PUBLISHER

Portland, Maine

# User's Guide
## to
## Walch Reproducible Books

As part of our general effort to provide educational materials which are as practical and economical as possible, we have designated this publication a "reproducible book." The designation means that purchase of the book includes purchase of the right to limited reproduction of all pages on which this symbol appears:

Here is the basic Walch policy: We grant to individual purchasers of this book the right to make sufficient copies of reproducible pages for use by all students of a single teacher. This permission is limited to a single teacher, and does not apply to entire schools or school systems, so institutions purchasing the book should pass the permission on to a single teacher. Copying of the book or its parts for resale is prohibited.

Any questions regarding this policy or requests to purchase further reproduction rights should be addressed to:

Permissions Editor
J. Weston Walch, Publisher
321 Valley Street • P. O. Box 658
Portland, Maine 04104-0658

---

## Credits

| | |
|---|---|
| Corel CD | pages 18, 27, 33, 59, 114 |
| Wildside Press CD | page 61 |

---

1   2   3   4   5   6   7   8   9   10

ISBN 0-8251-3284-3

Copyright © 1997 Beatrice Lumpkin
J. Weston Walch, Publisher
P. O. Box 658 • Portland, Maine 04104-0658

Printed in the United States of America

# Contents

# Introduction

## GOALS

This book provides multicultural, classroom-ready resources for algebra teachers and students. The goals of this book are:

1. To enrich the algebra curriculum with real-life examples from many cultures, including African American, Latino, Native American, Pacific Islander, and Asian—cultures that are often underrepresented in the mathematics curriculum.

2. To help students gain pride in their own heritage and to learn respect for other cultures.

## ALGEBRA AS A GATEKEEPER

Mathematics educators have recognized the importance of mastering algebra early, to open the "gate" to careers in mathematics, science, engineering, and business. Special efforts are under way to correct underrepresentation of minorities and women in these fields, including projects such as the early mastery of algebra promoted by the National Science Foundation's Urban Initiative. The importance of algebra is also acknowledged in the *Curriculum and Evaluation Standards for School Mathematics:* "Algebra is the language through which most of mathematics is communicated."

## MULTICULTURAL ORIGINS OF ALGEBRA

Students can gain confidence in their own ability to master algebra when they learn about the multicultural origins of algebra. Algebra was developed by people from many countries. Students can be proud of the contributions to mathematics made by their own ancestors.

*Algebra* is an Arabic word, a different spelling of the *al-jabr* books that brought algebra to Europe about 1200 years ago. These algebra books were written in Arabic by Islamic scholars from central Asia, Arabia, Turkey, North Africa, and Spain. The Islamic scholars included Muslims, Jews, and Christians. However, 3000 years earlier, ancient Egyptians and Babylonians had already invented algebra to solve the problems of everyday life. Indeed, many scholars believe that mathematics developed over 100,000 years ago with the beginning of the human race in Africa.

## SCOPE OF THIS BOOK

This book includes material of interest to algebra students from grades 7 to 12. For the convenience of the classroom teacher, contributions of different cultures are presented by algebraic topic. In the first section, number systems from Africa, Asia, and the Americas are considered. Other multicultural contributions are presented under the usual algebraic topics, from linear equations, proportion and variation, coordinates, and quadratic equations, to radicals and exponents, series, probability, and statistics.

## COOPERATIVE LEARNING AND MANIPULATIVES

A substantial number of hands-on activities and class or group projects make algebra come alive for students. Most activities in this book encourage cooperative learning. The manipulatives that are suggested are all inexpensive and readily available. The use of manipulatives repeats the actual history of mathematics—of experimentation to solve problems of real life.

## HOW TO USE THIS BOOK

Chapters on problem solving are suitable for use throughout the school year. Other units follow the usual algebra sequence. The teacher can easily find a choice of multicultural material relevant to the algebra topic of interest. Units begin with one or two pages of background information, followed by questions to encourage critical thinking. Each unit concludes with problems to solve or activities and projects to construct. Answers to Questions for Critical Thinking appear on the Teacher Guide pages at the beginning of each chapter.

A bibliography for further reading is included.

# African Number Systems

## Early African Calendars

### MATERIALS

Reproducible 1

### ANSWERS

1. Answers will vary.

2. Answers will vary.

3. 1461 years

4. 19 days; not too noticeable

5. (a) 112.5 days

   (b) Answers will vary; some added a thirteenth month to some lunar years.

## Measuring Lengths Along the Nile River

### MATERIALS

Length of cord or string
small piece of masking tape
Reproducible 2

### PROCEDURE

1. Divide class into pairs and distribute the handout.

2. Have students work as directed on the handout to find the length of the Nile from Cairo to Aswan.

3. After students have compared their findings, have them discuss the differences. What reasons might there be for different findings?

### ANSWERS

3. ≈ 9.5 cm

4. Approximately 600 miles, 965 km

5. Answers will vary.

## Measuring the Height of Nile Floods with Cubits

### MATERIALS

30-inch strip of paper (adding machine tape works well)
meterstick
cubit pattern from page 8
Reproducible 3

### PROCEDURE

1. Divide the class into groups and distribute the handout.

2. Have students work as directed on handouts to find personal cubit, finger, palm lengths.

3. After students have completed their measurements, have them compare and discuss their findings with those of students in the other groups. Why are there differences? How do the students' measurements compare with the royal cubit?

4. Discuss with students the need for standard measurements.

### ANSWERS

Comparison of 0.1 cm and $\frac{1}{16}$ finger:
   The accuracy is close to the same because 0.1 cm = .001 m

1 cubit = 28 fingers
.525 m = 525 mm
$$\frac{.525 \text{ meters}}{1 \text{ cubit}} = \frac{525 \text{ mm}}{28 \text{ fingers}}$$

There are 448 (28 × 16) $\frac{1}{16}$ fingers per cubit. Therefore, $\frac{1}{16}$ finger equals ≈ 1.17 mm or .60117 m

They have about equal accuracy.

## Early Egyptian Numerals

### MATERIALS

Reproducible 4

### ANSWERS

1. ∩∩∩∩∩||| = 53

   @@@∩∩∩∩| = 341

   ⌇⌇∩∩∩∩∩∩∩||| = 2073

   ⌇⌇⌇@@∩∩∩∩∩∩ = 30,260

2. 146 = @∩∩∩∩||||||

   2200 = ⌇⌇@@

   10,023 = ⌇ ∩∩|||

   2,340,000 = 𓁿 𓁿 ⌇⌇⌇ ⌇⌇⌇⌇

   5000 = ⌇⌇⌇⌇⌇

   100,301 = ⌇@@@|

## Egyptian Script Numerals – The First Ciphers

### MATERIALS

Reproducible 5

### PROCEDURE

1. Distribute the handout.

2. If you wish, divide students into groups. Deciphering hieratic numerals is a little like trying to read someone's handwriting—the figures as they're

actually formed may be quite different from the model. Working collaboratively should make this process less frustrating.

3. Have students figure out the hieratic numerals.

4. Encourage student discussion of the relative advantages of hieroglyphic and hieratic numerals.

### ANSWERS

| | | |
|---|---|---|
| 1. 7 | 4. 2401 |
| 2. 49 | 5. 16,807 |
| 3. 343 | 6. 19,607 |

## Building the Pyramids

### MATERIALS

Reproducible 6

### PROCEDURE

1. Distribute the handout.

2. Have students proceed as directed.

### ANSWERS

1. (a) 25 + 2 = 27 cubits

   (b) Answers will vary. Add two numbers with the same sign, add absolute values and keep the sign.

2. (a) 0–10–15 = –27 cubits

   (b) same as (b) above

3. (a) 5 × +2 = +10 cubits

   (b) Multiply like signs, result is +

4. (a) 7 $(-\frac{1}{2})$ = $-3\frac{1}{2}$ cubits

   (b) Multiply unlike signs, result is negative

5.  (a)  20 – (–5) = 25 courses

(b)  To subtract a number, change its
sign. Then follow rules for addition.

## The Egyptian Zero

### MATERIALS

Reproducible 7

### PROCEDURE

1.  Distribute the handout.

2.  Have students proceed as directed.

### ANSWERS

Answers will vary—there may be no
answers, too.

## The Wolof Number System

### MATERIALS

Reproducible 8

### ANSWERS

1.  (a)  juroom niet, juroom = fook ak niet

(b)  juroom niet, juroom benn = fook ak
nient

2.  5 + 1 = 6   5 + 2 = 7   5 + 3 = 8

3.  (a)  50:  juroom fook

(b)  60:  juroom benn fook

4.  (a)  20 + 50:  niar fook, juroom fook =
juroom niar fook

(b)  30 + 60:  niet fook, juroom benn fook
= juroom nient fook

5.  Answers will vary.

6.  Answers will vary.

### EXTENSION

The country of Senegal—like several other
West African nations—uses the franc CFA as its
currency. In 1997, the exchange rate was 489.22
francs CFA to the U.S. dollar. Either find the
current rate of exchange or give students the
1997 rate. Ask students to calculate the prices
in francs CFA of the items listed in the group
activity.

## Yoruba Numbers

### MATERIALS

Reproducible 9

### ANSWERS

1.  2 (20) – 5

2.  2 (20) – 2

3.  2 (20) + 4

4.  3 (20) – 10 + 3

5.  3 (20) – 3

6.  4 (20)

7.  5 (20)

8.  6(20) – 5

# Early African Calendars

## LONGEST RIVER

The Nile River of Africa is 4160 miles, or 6656 km, long—the longest river in the world. Its waters drain $\frac{1}{10}$ of the area of Africa, including parts of present-day Egypt, Sudan, Ethiopia, Uganda, and Rwanda. The Nile Valley gave life to two of the world's first civilizations, the related cultures of Egypt and Nubia.

The growth of civilization led to a rapid growth of mathematics and science. People have always looked for patterns in the world around them, patterns that they could use. They found a very important pattern in the seasonal changes of the Nile River.

**Earliest water clock, from Egypt, 1500 BCE**

Once a year, the Nile River changes dramatically. For most of the year, the White Nile quietly joins the Blue Nile to form the great Nile River at Khartoum, in Sudan. But at the end of August, there is a sudden change. Heavy rains in the highlands of Ethiopia wash floodwaters and silt into the Blue Nile. The Blue Nile swells to twice its usual size and turns the Nile River into a roaring flood. The flood rushes north, plunging over six cataracts.

Nowadays, the floodwaters are held in the artificial Lake Nasser and released year-round to turn electric generators and water crops. But it was different in ancient times. The flood used to rush downhill over 1000 miles, through Nubia and Egypt to the Mediterranean Sea. The land near the river was flooded for weeks. People were glad to see the flood, because it brought water for their crops. When the river went down, it left a rich silt that fertilized the fields. Rain was rare. The desert took over on the high ground where the floodwaters did not reach. For people of the Nile Valley, the timing of the flood was of the greatest importance.

## FLOOD AND STAR

Thousands of years ago, African scientists began to count the number of days between the beginning of one Nile flood and the next. They kept these records for hundreds of years. Their records showed that, on average, there were 365 days between floods. Astronomers made another exciting discovery. They noticed that the bright star Sirius reappeared in the sky as the Nile floodwaters neared Memphis in Egypt. The same thing happened after 365 days, and again after another 365 days.

The study of star and flood patterns led the Egyptians to design the first 365-day, solar calendar. The official Egyptian calendar had 12 months with 30 days to each month. They added five days for New Year celebrations to make a year of 365 days. A later pharaoh added a leap day every four years to make the average year $365\frac{1}{4}$ days long.

## LUNAR CALENDAR, SOLAR CALENDAR

The Egyptian government still kept the old lunar calendar to mark religious holidays. Lunar calendars are based on the 29.5-day moon cycle. (Even today, people use lunar calendars to find the

*(continued)*

# Early African Calendars *(continued)*

date of the Christian Easter or the Jewish Passover or the Muslim Ramadan.) Unfortunately, lunar calendars were very complicated; 12 months of 29 days made a year that was 17 days short of 365. To make up for the short 12-month years, some lunar years had to have 13 months.

When Julius Caesar came to Egypt to visit the pharaoh Cleopatra, he became acquainted with the 365-day Egyptian calendar. It was the only calendar that had the same number of months each year. Julius Caesar took the 365-day calendar back with him to Europe where it became known as the Julian calendar. Its Egyptian origin was forgotten.

The ancient Egyptians were also first to divide the day into 24 hours, 12 hours of night and 12 hours of day. At first the hours of day and night varied with the season, but later the Egyptians made all the hours of equal length.

## Questions for Critical Thinking

1. There is evidence that people used lunar calendars long before writing was invented. Without modern numerals, how could you keep track of the number of days in a month?

2. The Egyptian calendar had 12 months, each 30 days long. Each month had 3 weeks of 10 days. To make 365 days for the year, the Egyptians added 5 days of New Year's holidays. Compare their calendar to ours. Which do you prefer and why?

3. The New Year would start on day 1 the first time the calendar was used. But the 365-day calendar ends the year $\frac{1}{4}$ day too soon. How many years would it take before a New Year's Day would fall on the right day again? Complete this table to find the answer.

| Years Calendar Is in Use | Days That New Year Is Early |
|---|---|
| 1 year | $\frac{1}{4}$ day |
| 100 years | 25 days |
| 1000 years | 250 days |
| _____ years | $365\frac{1}{4}$ days |

4. Without a leap day every four years, a 365-day calendar would slowly drift away from the natural seasons. How many days would it drift in a lifetime of 76 years? Do you think this drift would be noticeable?

5. A lunar year has 354 days (6 months of 29 days and 6 months of 30 days). A solar year has about $365\frac{1}{4}$ days.

   (a) In 10 years, how many days would the lunar calendar lag behind the solar calendar?

   (b) How would you adjust the lunar calendar to agree with the solar calendar?

*Algebra Activities from Many Cultures*

# Measuring Lengths along the Nile River

**Directions:** Find the length of the river from Cairo to Aswan. Check off each step as you complete it.

❏  1. Tape the thread at Cairo, then along the length of the river on the map, letting the cord make all of the bends as shown.

❏  2. Mark the point on the thread where it reaches Aswan.

❏  3. Straighten the thread. Measure the marked length in centimeters.

Marked length = _____ cm

❏  4. Calculate the river length from Cairo to Aswan by using this proportion:

$$\frac{\text{River length, Cairo-Aswan}}{\text{Thread length in cm}} = \frac{\text{no. km}}{1\ \text{cm}}$$

❏  5. Compare your result from step 4 with results of other students in the class. How close to the actual length was your measurement?

## Discussion:

What are possible causes for differences in measurements?

On this map of the Nile River, the scale is about 75 km/cm.

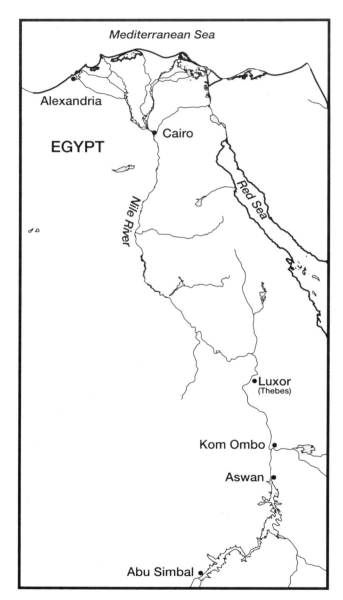

**The Nile River in Ancient Times**

*Algebra Activities from Many Cultures*

# Measuring the Height of Nile Floods with Cubits

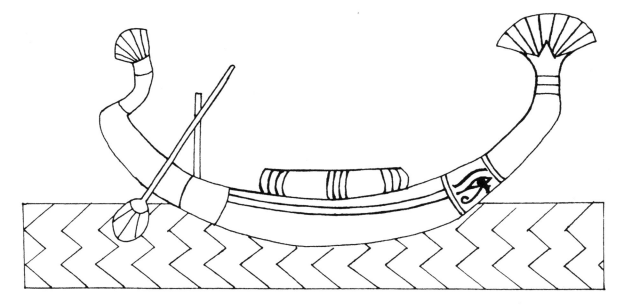

The prosperity of the Nile Valley farmers depended on the height of the annual flood. A low flood would leave some fields high and dry and people would go hungry. Too high a flood would wash out irrigation works and ruin the villages.

## PATTERNS: EARLY STATISTICS

For thousands of years clerks and surveyors, called scribes, measured and recorded the height of the Nile flood. This was the beginning of statistics. In statistics, numerical values are collected and studied to see if there is a pattern to them.

To measure the height of the flood, Egyptians used a vertical stick, or a tower, marked in cubits. The cubit was the unit of length used in the Nile Valley, Palestine, and Babylonia. The royal cubit was based on the length of the forearm of some early pharaoh, or king of Egypt. Egyptians used that early pharoah's forearm as a standard measure. The forearm was measured from the point of the elbow to the tip of the middle finger.

*(continued)*

# Measuring the Height of Nile Floods with Cubits *(continued)*

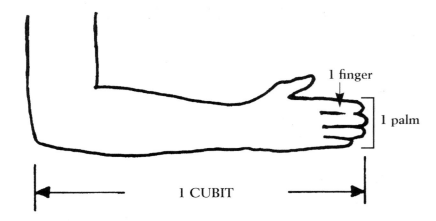

| Egyptian Units of Length |
| --- |
| **Cubit:**  The length of a forearm, from elbow to extended fingertips. |
| **Palm:**  The outstretched hand, without the thumb—there are seven palms to one royal cubit. |
| **Finger:**  There are four fingers to one palm, and 28 fingers to one royal cubit. |

## Your Personal Cubit

**Directions:**  With your group, solve and discuss the following problems. Check off each step as you complete it.

1. How many 4-finger palms are there in your personal cubit?

❏　　Measure with your 4-finger palms from your elbow to your middle fingertip.

❏　　Compare with others in your group.

**Discussion:**

The royal cubit had 7 palms. Did you get 7? What does that tell you about the old pharaoh's build? Do you think he was short and stocky or tall and slender?

2. Measure a length with your personal cubits, palms, and fingers.

❏　　Each member of your group should use his or her personal cubits, palms, and fingers to measure the length of the same desk. Record each member's measurement.

❏　　Compare your measurement of the desk with the values found by others in your group.

*(continued)*

*Algebra Activities from Many Cultures*

# Measuring the Height of Nile Floods with Cubits *(continued)*

## Discussion:

Are your readings the same? If not, why are there differences? Why are standard measures needed?

3. Compare the royal cubit and the meter.

❑ Draw a royal cubit scale, 52.5 cm long. Divide the cubit into 7 equal palms. Divide each palm into 4 equal fingers.

❑ Cut out your royal cubit and place it on a meterstick. Compare large and small divisions of lengths including centimeters (0.01 of a meter) and fingers ($\frac{1}{28}$ of a cubit). Optional: If you wish, you can decorate your cubit stick with Egyptian hieroglyphs and symbols.

## Discussion:

For finer measure, fingers were divided into halves, thirds, fourths, down to sixteenths. How well does the accuracy of a cubit scale compare to the modern meter scale? Use the value of 1 cubit = .525 m for your comparison.

The smallest unit marked on the meter scale is usually 0.1 cm.

The smallest unit marked on the cubit scale is $\frac{1}{16}$ finger.

Compare 0.1 cm (.001 m) to $\frac{1}{16}$ finger.

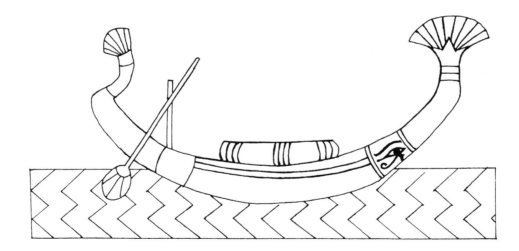

*Algebra Activities from Many Cultures*

# Early Egyptian Numerals

As wealth and population grew in the Nile Valley, a central government formed under King Narmer. Here's an outline on one of his maceheads from about 3100 B.C.E. It shows an early census of the Nile Delta region. The census lists 120,000 enemies taken prisoner. There are 1,422,000 goats, and 400,000 cattle.

The earliest counting system developed in Egypt used tally marks: one stroke for 1, ten strokes for 10, one hundred strokes for 100. Can you imagine writing the numbers from this census with tally marks? A better way to record large numbers was needed. Egyptian numerals were developed to meet this need.

Detail from King Narmer's macehead, adapted from N.B. Millet and Barbara Ibronyi

## TALLY MARKS IN THE NEW SYSTEM

Tallies were still used for Egyptian numerals 1 through 9:

I  II  III  IIII  IIIII  IIIIII  IIIIIII  IIIIIIII  IIIIIIIII

## NUMBER SYMBOLS INVENTED

But for 10, some geniuses had a brilliant idea. They said, "Let's use one symbol to stand for 10 tallies. Instead of writing IIIIIIIIII, let's use a heel bone sign, ∩."

For 11, they wrote ∩I. For 12, ∩II, and so on, up to 19, ∩IIIIIIIII.

Then 20 was ∩∩, 30 was ∩∩∩ and so on up to 99. For 99, they repeated ones and tens until they added to 99: ∩∩∩∩∩∩∩∩∩IIIIIIIII.

For larger numbers, they invented new symbols for powers of 10 up to 1,000,000. A different symbol was used for each power of 10.

*(continued)*

*Algebra Activities from Many Cultures*

# Early Egyptian Numerals *(continued)*

| Hieroglyphic Numerals | | |
| --- | --- | --- |
| Modern Numeral | Egyptian Hieroglyphic Numeral | Picture |
| 1 | I | tally mark |
| 10 | ∩ | heel |
| 100 | @ | coil of rope |
| 1000 | 🪷 | lotus flower |
| 10,000 | 𓂭 | finger |
| 100,000 | 𓆐 | bird or tadpole |
| 1,000,000 | 𓀠 | man, arms raised |

Hieroglyphic numerals are additive. That makes them easy to read. You just add together the value of each symbol. To read the number 🪷@I, you would find the value of each symbol—1000, 100, 1—and add them together. So 🪷@I = 1000 + 100 + 1 = 1101. Egyptians usually wrote from right to left—but not always.  Since the numerals are additive, they have the same value if they are written left to right, right to left, or top to bottom.

1. Check these examples with the table of hieroglyphic numerals. Then fill in the blanks to give the value of the examples below:

∩∩∩∩∩III              @@@∩∩∩∩I              🪷🪷∩∩∩∩∩∩∩III              𓂭 𓂭 𓂭@@∩∩∩∩∩∩

_____              _____              _____              _____

*(continued)*

# Early Egyptian Numerals *(continued)*

2. Write the hieroglyphic numeral equivalents for the numbers listed below.

146 _____

2200 _____

10,023 _____

2,340,000 _____

5000 _____

100,301 _____

## Group Discussion:

What are some of the differences between Egyptian and modern numerals?

*Note:* Did you know that modern numerals are also multicultural in origin? The numerals we use are called Indo-Arabic numerals. The symbols 1 through 9 and the use of place value came from India. Arabic-speaking mathematicians introduced the decimal fractions.

*Algebra Activities from Many Cultures*

# Egyptian Script Numerals

## The First Ciphers

Egyptian hieroglyphs were easy to read, but scribes wanted something that was easier to write. So they invented a simplified script, called *hieratic*. Egyptian mathematics books were written in the quick hieratic script. Hieratic numerals used a different principle than hieroglyphic numerals. Instead of repeating tally marks, hieratic numerals used separate symbols for the numbers from 1 to 9. Easy-to-write symbols were also invented for tens, 10 through 90, hundreds, 100 through 900, and so on. Modern numerals use this old African idea of symbols or ciphers instead of tallies that repeat.

| Hieratic Numerals | | | | | | | | | |
|---|---|---|---|---|---|---|---|---|---|
| | 1 | 2 | 3 | 4 | 5 | 6 | 7 | 8 | 9 |
| Units | | | | | | | | | |
| Tens | | | | | | | | | |
| Hundreds | | | | | | | | | |
| Thousands | | | | | | | | | |
| Tens of thousands | | | | | | | | | |

Adapted from Gillings, 1972, and Boyer, 1944

*(continued)*

*Algebra Activities from Many Cultures*

# Egyptian Script Numerals *(continued)*

## READ HIERATIC NUMERALS

These hieratic numerals are adapted from a mathematical papyrus written by the scribe Ah'mose. Find their equivalent in modern numerals from the pictured table. Notice that Egyptian script was usually written from right to left. Naturally, to write the equivalent modern numerals, you will write from left to right. Also, write the numbers as hieroglyphic numerals. *Hint:* The numbers are powers of the first number. The last number is the sum.

1. _____

2. _____

3. _____

4. _____

5. _____

6. _____

*Algebra Activities from Many Cultures*

# Building the Pyramids

## The First Number Line

African pyramids have fascinated people for almost 5000 years. People wonder, "Why were they built? What secrets are buried inside them? How were they built without modern machines?" We shall probably never know all the answers to these questions. But we do know that the Africans who built the pyramids used a lot of mathematics.

To support the tremendous weight of stone, pyramids needed a good foundation and careful planning. We can still see some ancient pyramid plans drawn on the foundation walls. Some lines gave the slope of the pyramid. Other construction guidelines were drawn parallel to the ground for use as leveling lines.

To measure heights above and below ground, pyramid builders used a reference line, often at ground level. The line was labeled *nefer*, the Egyptian word for zero. (*Nefer* was also the word for beauty.) Above the *nefer* reference line, a series of leveling

| |
|---|
| 7 cubits above zero |
| 6 cubits above zero |
| 5 cubits above zero |
| 4 cubits above zero |
| 2 cubits above zero |
| 3 cubits above zero |
| 2 cubits above zero |
| 1 cubit above zero |
| 1 cubit below zero |
| 2 cubits below zero |
| 3 cubits below zero |
| 4 cubits below zero |
| 5 cubits below zero |
| 6 cubits below zero |

ground level (zero)

lines were drawn. They were spaced one cubit apart and labeled "one cubit above zero, two cubits above zero, three cubits above zero," and so on. Leveling lines below ground were labeled "one cubit below zero, two cubits below zero, three cubits below zero, four cubits below zero," and so on.

These ancient Africans had discovered the set of numbers that we call integers. These are the numbers we write as $\{. . . -3, -2, -1, 0, 1, 2, . . .\}$. The vertical line at right angles to the horizontal guidelines on this page is a true number line. Numbers above ground or zero level can be considered positive. Values below ground can be represented as negative.

## SIGNED NUMBERS

### Questions for Critical Thinking

Suppose you are an engineer at a pyramid construction site.

1. Your team starts at a level 25 cubits above zero. By the end of the month, you add 2 cubits of height to the pyramid.

   (a) How high will the pyramid be? Show your calculation using signed numbers.

*(continued)*

*Algebra Activities from Many Cultures*

# Building the Pyramids *(continued)*

(b) What rule for signed numbers did you use?

_____

2. The king's body is in the stone coffin, at ground level, ready to be eased down the burial shaft in the pyramid. Your team slowly lowers the stone coffin down 10 cubits. Then another team lowers the coffin 15 cubits.

(a) How far below ground will the coffin be? Show your calculation using signed numbers.

_____

(b) What rule for signed numbers did you use?

_____

3. You have worked on the pyramid for five months and your team adds 2 cubits of height to the pyramid each month.

(a) At the end of five months, how much did the height of the pyramid increase? Show your calculation using signed numbers.

_____

(b) What rule for signed numbers did you use?

_____

4. You are digging a foundation for a temple. Each day your team digs down $\frac{1}{2}$ cubit.

(a) At the end of seven days, how far down have you dug?

_____

(b) What rule for signed numbers did you use?

_____

5. You wish to build a wall that is 20 cubits above ground, using stones that are 1 cubit high. You start the wall in a foundation trench 5 cubits below ground.

(a) How many courses of stone (rows of stone) will you need? Show your calculation, using signed numbers.

_____

(b) What rule for signed numbers did you use?

_____

*(continued)*

# Building the Pyramids (continued)

## NUMBER LINES AT THE PYRAMIDS

### Group Project

**Directions:** Work with your group on the following project. Check off each step as you complete it.

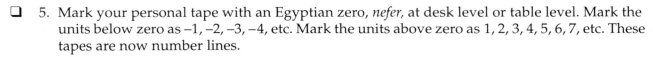

❑  1. Carefully unroll and tear off a length of about $2\frac{1}{4}$ meters of masking tape for each person in the group.

❑  2. Place all the lengths of tape, sticky side down, on a table or desk. For each member of the group, start at one end and mark off distances equal to the width of four fingers of the palm of your left hand. Write the group member's name at the end of the tape, and remove from the disk.

❑  3. Tie the weight to the end of the string to make a plumb line.

❑  4. Have one member of the group let the plumb line hang down near a wall to get a true vertical line. Apply the length of tape marked with your personal palm widths to the wall, using the vertical plumb line as your guide.

❑  5. Mark your personal tape with an Egyptian zero, *nefer*, at desk level or table level. Mark the units below zero as –1, –2, –3, –4, etc. Mark the units above zero as 1, 2, 3, 4, 5, 6, 7, etc. These tapes are now number lines.

❑  6. Line up all the tapes in your group so that the zero marks are all on the same horizontal line. Stretch a piece of tape across the zero marks of several tapes to create a ground, or zero-reference, line. (Egyptians used an A-level for this step.)

## Discussion

Pyramid builders used horizontal guidelines spaced 1 cubit apart. Since there are 7 palms to 1 cubit, the first cubit above zero should be 7 palms above the zero marks. Would you get a horizontal cubit line if you ran a length of tape across the +7 marks on all the students' number-line tapes? Investigate. Why or why not?

Why did builders have to standardize their measures?

The plumb line provides a true vertical guide line. How can you be sure that your horizontal lines are truly horizontal?

*Algebra Activities from Many Cultures*

# The Egyptian Zero

Some people think that the pyramid builders were the greatest engineers in history. They kept tens of thousands of people working without stepping on one another's toes. Food and water had to be carried in and handed out to thousands of workers. Records had to be kept of all the supplies that were needed and the wages paid to the workers. Thousands of engineers, bookkeepers, and mathematicians were needed.

When you think of all those records, it is not surprising that an Egyptian bookkeeper was the first to think of zero as a number that could answer this question:

"What is the remainder if 7 is subtracted from 7?"

The Egyptian bookkeeper's answer was "*nefer,*" the same symbol that they had used for the zero ground line. *Nefer* was the Egyptian symbol for beauty, or "completed," and was an abstraction of the human windpipe, lungs, and heart.

Egyptian pyramid

## Discussion

1. Do you think zero is a number?

Give examples of each of the following operations with zero. If you think an operation can be done with zero, give an example. If you think it cannot be done, give a *counterexample*—an example of an operation that does not work.

2. Can you add zero?

   *Example or counterexample:* _____

3. Can you subtract zero?

   *Example or counterexample:* _____

4. Can you multiply by zero?

   *Example or counterexample:* _____

5. Can you divide by zero?

   *Example or counterexample:* _____

6. What other ways do you use zero?

_____

*Algebra Activities from Many Cultures*

# The Wolof Number System

Wolof is an African language widely spoken in Senegal, West Africa. The Wolof scientist Cheikh Anta Diop showed that the mathematical terms Wolof people use today closely resemble ancient Egyptian words. That is not surprising; Wolof and the ancient Egyptian language belong to the same family of languages. To show that the Wolof language was as flexible and advanced as any European language, Diop translated part of Albert Einstein's work on relativity into Wolof.

Like the Egyptian number system, the Wolof number system is decimal—based on 10. Wolof numbers also have a subbase of 5. This simplifies addition with Wolof numbers.

The table below shows some Wolof number words.

| | | |
|---|---|---|
| one (1) — benn | eight (8) — juroom niet | 15 — fook ak juroom |
| two (2) — niar | nine (9) — juroom nient | 16 — fook ak juroom benn |
| three (3) — niet | ten (10) — fook | 17 — fook ak juroom niar |
| four (4) — nient | 11 — fook ak benn | 18 — fook ak juroom niet |
| five (5) — juroom | 12 — fook ak niar | 19 — fook ak juroom nient |
| six (6) — juroom benn | 13 — fook ak niet | 20 — niar fook |
| seven (7) — juroom niar | 14 — fook ak nient | |

Multiples of 10 are regular. For example:  30—niet fook, 40—nient fook.

## WOLOF NUMBERS

### Questions for Critical Thinking

Work with a partner on the following problems.

1. Translate these number words into Wolof and give the sums in Wolof.

    (a) 8 + 5 _____

    (b) 8 + 6 _____

2. How are the Wolof words for six, seven, eight, and nine related to their word for five?

    _____

3. Follow the pattern used for 30 and 40 to write the Wolof words for:

    (a) 50 _____

    (b) 60 _____

*(continued)*

# The Wolof Number System *(continued)*

4. Translate these number words into Wolof and give the sums in Wolof.

   (a) 20 + 50 _____

   (b) 30 + 60 _____

5. How do our number words for 13 to 40 show that we use a base-10 number system?

   _____

6. Look for patterns in the Wolof number words on page 19. Can you find any overall pattern? As simply as you can, describe how Wolof number words are formed.

   _____

   _____

## Class Activity

The main language spoken in Senegal today is Wolof. However, many neighbors of the Wolof speak other languages. When they meet in the marketplace, buyers and sellers often communicate with hand signals. One signal stands for 1, another for 2, and so on. Signals also are used for "less," "more," "yes," "no," and any other words needed to express what the buyer and seller need to say. Often the seller demands twice the price she or he expects. The buyer, in turn, offers only one half the price he or she is willing to pay. There is a lot of good-humored debate and finally a deal is made.

**Directions:** Form four groups, each a different "language group." Let each group meet and invent its own set of hand signals for numbers 1 to 50. Then groups can take turns presenting their system of hand signals to see if the other language groups can understand the signals.

Transactions could include the following items, with asking prices as listed. You could also make up your own examples.

1. A Senegalese cotton dress for $20

2. An African mathematical game board, called *wari*, for $12

3. A 21-string Wolof musical instrument, called *kora*, for $49

4. A sand painting by an art student for $36

*Algebra Activities from Many Cultures*

# Yoruba Numbers

Most African Americans are descended from the people of West Africa, people with a proud heritage. The wealth of West Africa came from agriculture, skilled crafts, and trade. Great empires rose—Ghana, Mali, Songhay, Oyo, and others. It was said that the King of Ghana could put 200,000 warriors into battle. Mathematics was developed to keep track of the large armies, to figure out the taxes, and to control the gold and salt trade.

The Yoruba of Nigeria are one of the great West African peoples. Their number system was developed to meet the demands of a complex economy. The Yoruba had special names for one to ten, for twenty, thirty, two hundred, and four hundred. All other numbers were multiples or combinations of these numbers.

| Yoruba System of Numbers | |
|---|---|
| 1 through 10 | special names |
| 10 through 14 | 10, 10 + 1, 10 + 2, 10 + 3, 10 + 4 |
| 15 through 19 | 20 − 5, 20 − 4, 20 − 3, 20 − 2, 20 − 1 |
| 20 through 24 | 20, 20 + 1, 20 + 2, 20 + 3, 20 + 4 |
| 25 through 29 | 30 − 5, 30 − 4, 30 − 3, 30 − 2, 30 − 1 |
| 30 through 34 | 30, 30 + 1, 30 + 2, 30 + 3, 30 + 4 |
| 40 | two 20's |
| 45 | three 20's − 10 − 5 |
| 50 | three 20's − 10 |
| 60 | three 20's |

## Group Discussion

Study the pattern of numbers used by the Yoruba. Follow the pattern to show how the following numbers are composed:

1. 35 _____

2. 38 _____

3. 44 _____

4. 53 _____

5. 57 _____

6. 80 _____

7. 100 _____

8. 115 _____

*Algebra Activities from Many Cultures*

# Mesopotamian Number Systems

## Numerals from Babylonia

### MATERIALS

Reproducible 10

### BACKGROUND

[to come]

### ANSWERS

1. 7223 and 8580

2. Base 10

3.

$$\rhd \triangledown \triangledown$$
$$\rhd \triangledown \triangledown \quad (34) \qquad \triangledown \triangledown \quad \triangledown \quad (121)$$
$$\rhd \triangledown \triangledown$$

$$\triangledown \triangledown \triangledown \ \triangledown \triangledown \triangledown \ (305) \quad \triangledown \quad \triangledown \quad \rhd \ (3670)$$
$$\triangledown \triangledown \qquad \triangledown \triangledown$$

4. Seconds in a minute, minutes in an hour, degrees in an angle.

## Babylonian Mathematical Tablet: A Project

### MATERIALS

for each student or group:  Mexican self-hardening pottery clay
wood chopstick with one end sharpened to a stylus with a wedge-shaped tip
Reproducible 11

### OVERVIEW

Students will create a table showing a group of consecutive numbers, their squares, and their cubes, then write the cuneiform equivalent of these numerals in the clay.

### PROCEDURE

1. Distribute the handout.

2. Have students proceed as directed on the handout, using the illustrations of cuneiform numerals as a guide.

### EXTENSION ACTIVITY

Divide class into small groups. Direct each group to prepare a multiplication table for base 60 numerals.

# Numerals from Babylonia

Over 5000 years ago in the land now called Iraq, the Sumerian people built great cities and temples. They invented a unique way of writing with a stylus on clay tablets. When Babylonians became the rulers of the land, they adopted the Sumerian writing, called cuneiform.

To write Babylonian numerals, the stylus was held upright to make a vertical wedge mark for units. The Babylonian numerical system used a base of 60. For tens, the stylus was held at an angle to make a horizontal mark. Up to 59, the tally principle was used to repeat enough ones and tens to add up to the desired value.

| **Units** | **Tens** | **59** |
|-----------|----------|--------|

## POSITIONAL VALUE

For 60, the scribes had a brilliant idea. In a great stroke of genius, they moved the stylus across to a new place, a 60's place. Each unit in the new place would count for 60. For example, two units in the 60's place would equal 120. The next place value was $60^2$, or 3600. This was the first place-value system of numerals in history.

Here are some examples of Babylonian numerals.

| $2 \times 10 + 5$ | $5 \times 10 + 6$ | $12 \times 60 + 32$ | $3 \times 3600 + 1 \times 60 + 4 \times 10$ |
|---|---|---|---|
| 25 | 56 | 752 | 108,100 |

*(continued)*

*Algebra Activities from Many Cultures*

# Numerals from Babylonia *(continued)*

▰◁▰◁▰◁▰◁▰◁▰◁▰◁▰◁▰◁▰◁▰◁▰◁▰◁▰◁▰◁▰◁

## Questions for Critical Thinking

1. In Babylonia, 143, 7223, and 8580 were written as a sum of powers of 60. Place value was used for thousands of years, but there was no zero placeholder.

   $143 = 2 \times 60 + 23$         $7223 = 2 \times 3600 + 0 \times 60 + 23$         $8580 = 2 \times 3600 + 23 \times 60 + 0$

   ▽▽ ▷▽▽▽                        ▽▽ ▷▽▽▽                              ▽▽ ▷▽▽▽
      ▷                              ▷                                    ▷

   Which two of these numbers could be confused for lack of a zero placeholder?

   _____

2. What subbase do you see used in the Babylonian numerals of question 1?

   _____

3. Write the equivalent of these modern Indo-Arabic numerals, using Babylonian numerals:

   34 _____         121 _____

   305 _____         3670 _____

4. Can you think of any common units of measurement that still use base 60?

   _____

# Babylonian Mathematical Tablet

## A Project

### Goal

The goal of this project is to create a mathematical tablet, using Babylonian base-60 cuneiform numerals. Check off each step as you complete it.

☐ 1. Cut and form the clay to a smooth, 1-cm-thick sheet, with a surface about 10 cm × 15 cm.

☐ 2. With pencil and paper, make a table with three columns. The first column could be consecutive integers, perhaps 6 to 18. The second column would be the squares of the integers, and the third column would be their cubes. Next to the numerals, write in pencil the Babylonian equivalents in base 60.

| | integers | | squares | | cubes |
|---|---|---|---|---|---|
| 6 | 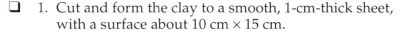 | 36 | | 216 | |
| 7 | | 49 | | 343 | |
| 8 | | 64 | | 512 | |

☐ 3. Use the stylus to press into the clay the Babylonian cuneiform numerals that you found in step 2. For units, press with the thin wedge edge vertically. For tens, press the tip of the stylus horizontally.

For 1 to 9, make vertical impressions.

For 10's, make horizontal impressions.

☐ 4. Allow to dry slowly. Self-hardening clay should be dry the next day.

*Algebra Activities from Many Cultures*

# Pre-Columbian Number Systems

## Number Systems of Central America

### MATERIALS

Reproducible 12

## Aztec Numerals

### MATERIALS

Reproducible 13

### BACKGROUND

According to Aztec legend, the Aztecs came originally from northern Mexico. In 1168 C.E., their god, Huitzilopochtli, told them to look for the site where they should build a city. They would know when they had found the place when they saw a sign: an eagle, perched on a cactus, holding a serpent in its claw. The Aztecs wandered through Mexico until 1325 C.E., when they finally found the sign and founded their city, Tenochtitlán, on Lake Texcoco. By the end of the fifteenth century, the Aztecs controlled a large empire in Central America. Some 150,000 people lived in Tenochtitlán, the Aztec capital. Food was grown on floating islands, call *chinampas*, built on the lake. When the Spaniards arrived in Tenochtitlán in 1519, they were amazed by the size and beauty of the city.

### ANSWERS

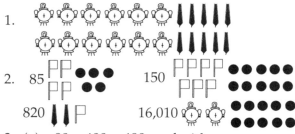

3. (a) 80 + 400 = 480 quahuitls
   (b) 220 + 200 = 420 quahuitls

(b)333,180

4.

675    480    266

## Maya Numerals

### MATERIALS

Reproducible 14

### BACKGROUND

The Maya civilization developed around 300 B.C. in what is now southern Mexico and Guatemala. The Maya created great city-states, built from stone, around the time that the Roman empire in Europe was crumbling. Although the number system shown on Reproducible 14 was used for many purposes, a different system was used for calculating the Maya calendar.

### ANSWERS

2. 3,199,999 years or $20^6 - 1$
3. Answers will vary.

## Calendars of Central America: The Least Common Multiple

### MATERIALS

Reproducible 15

### ANSWERS

1. 18,980 days, or 52 365-day years
2. 2920 days, or 8 365-day years
3. 37,960 days, or 104 365-day years
4. 2,391,480 days

# Number Systems of Central America

**Mexico City of today**

It was 1519. The Spanish army thought they were dreaming when they first saw Tenochtitlán, capital of the Aztec Empire. There was nothing like it in Europe for size, splendor, and cleanliness. The sunlit city, its buildings gleaming white, rose from the middle of Lake Texcoco. Straight roads, raised above lake level, connected the city to the mountains that surrounded it.

Mighty pyramids and temples flanked the great plazas of the site where Mexico City now stands. A sewer and water system and frequent baths safeguarded health and sanitation. Great markets served the needs of 50,000 customers a day. When trade disputes arose, they were settled peacefully by market courts according to Aztec laws.

The Aztec culture in Mexico followed a whole series of earlier cultures, including the Olmec, Maya, Zapotec, Toltec, and Mixtec. Mathematics, astronomy, agriculture, and medicine are some of the sciences that were developed by the people of Central America, many centuries before Columbus. Here are a few of their achievements in mathematics and astronomy.

1. **Zero symbol.** Central Americans used zero as a placeholder 1000 years before the Indo-Arabic zero reached Europe. The Maya zero symbol was a shell, which stood for goodness and completion. The Aztec symbol for zero was an ear of corn, or maize, which gave life to the people.

2. **Positional Value.** Most Central American numeral systems used positional value, based on twenty. Base-20 number systems were also used by the Taino and other indigenous people of Puerto Rico and Cuba.

3. **Accurate Calendars.** The solar calendar of 365 days was adjusted as needed for accuracy. A religious calendar of 260 days was meshed with the solar calendar to give a grand cycle of 52 years. Mathematics and centuries of work in astronomy were needed to design these calendars.

Name _____

Date _____

# Aztec Numerals

Since the Aztec books were burned by the invading Spanish army, our knowledge of Aztec mathematics is limited. The Nauhautl language, which is still alive among the Aztecs, gives us some insight into the Aztec number system. Surviving records of tribute paid to the Aztec empire and land records show two different systems of Aztec numerals. Both are based on powers of 20. (Instead of $10^0$, $10^1$, $10^2$, etc., they used $20^0$, $20^1$, $20^2$, etc.)

## ADDITIVE NUMERALS

An additive system of numerals was used in records of tribute paid to the Aztec empire:

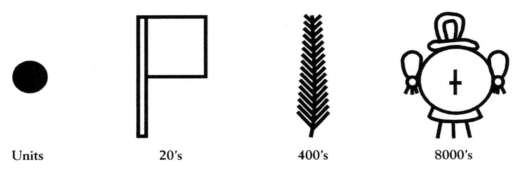

| Units | 20's | 400's | 8000's |
|---|---|---|---|

| | |
|---|---|
| 1 to 19 | A black dot stood for each unit. Dots were arranged in rows of 5. |
| 20's | A flag stood for 20, the whole person. Up to 19 flags, each with a value of 20, could be used. |
| 400's | A symbol for abundance, called *tzontli*. Up to 19 *tzontli*, each of value 400, could be used. |
| 8000's | A bag of 8000 cacao beans, also used as currency. |

**Examples:**

| 70 | 8040 | 200 bowls |
|---|---|---|

*(continued)*

*Algebra Activities from Many Cultures*

# Aztec Numerals *(continued)*

## POSITIONAL NUMERALS

Land records used another type of numerals: positional numerals. This system used place values. In these tax records, kept for tax purposes, farms are shown as rectangles. The unit of measure is the *quahuitl*. Farm area is given in square quahuitl measure written with positional numerals. There are three place-value positions inside the rectangle: units or $20^0$, 20's or $20^1$, and 400's or $20^2$. The positions are:

- **Upper right** for units 1 to 19, shown in a "bump" on the rectangle. If this position is empty, the bump is smoothed out to show a perfect rectangle.

- **Bottom** for 20's.

- **Center** for 400's. If the 400's position is empty, an ear of corn, the zero symbol, is placed in the top of the rectangle.

### Symbols

For units and 20's, vertical lines are used. Groups of five lines are tied together with a loop at the top. A dot is used for each 400. An ear of corn is a zero symbol placed in the top register if the 400's place is empty.

The following example is adapted from a tax record for two brothers.

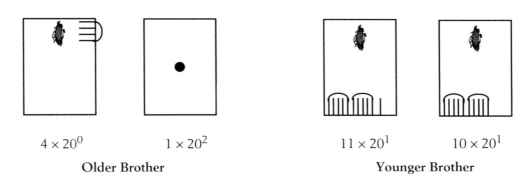

| $4 \times 20^0$ | $1 \times 20^2$ | $11 \times 20^1$ | $10 \times 20^1$ |
| :---: | :---: | :---: | :---: |
| **Older Brother** | | **Younger Brother** | |

Tax Record for Two Brothers
(Area of four fields given in square quahuitls)

*(continued)*

*Algebra Activities from Many Cultures*

Name _____

Date _____

# Aztec Numerals (*continued*)

## Questions for Critical Thinking

1.  Use additive Aztec numerals to show the population of Tenochtitlan (now Mexico City). In 1519, the population of Tenochtitlan was about 100,000.

2.  Use as many additive Aztec numerals as needed to make up the equivalent of the following values:

    85                                            150

    820                                           16,010

3.  Find the area of the two brothers' farms previously shown in the Aztec tax records. Give the area in square quahuitls. A quahuitl measures about 2.5 meters.

    (a)  The area of the older brothers' fields was _____ square quahuitls, and _____ square quahuitls.

    (b)  The area of the younger brothers' fields was _____ square quahuitls, and _____ square quahuitls.

4.  Use the positional Aztec numerals to show the following areas in square quahuitls.

    *Hint:* Draw a rectangle with the longer dimension vertical. Use the upper right corner for units, the bottom for 20's, and the center for 400's. Use vertical lines to show the values for units and 20's. Five vertical lines are joined on top.

    675                          480                          266

*Algebra Activities from Many Cultures*

# Maya Numerals

Millions of people still speak the Maya languages and preserve Maya culture. They are proud of the achievements of their ancestors in mathematics and the sciences. The Maya fought fiercely for their independence but they were defeated by the guns of the Spanish cavalry. Unfortunately, all but three or four of the Maya books were burned by the invaders as "works of the devil." However, the Maya numerals survived. We admire their efficient system of numerals, which included the earliest known use of a zero placeholder.

The Maya used a dot for one unit and repeated the dots until they reached four:

They wrote •, ••, •••, ••••.

For five, the complete hand, the Maya used a bar, ━ .

Finally, they counted by twenties, ten fingers and ten toes. This developed into a base-20 system, using powers of 20: $20^0, 20^1, 20^2$, and so on. They had the brilliant idea of using place value to write their numerals. We believe that the Maya were the first to use a a zero symbol to hold any place that was empty. Before this, an empty place in a place value system was left empty—like writing two hundred and three as 2   3. This often made place-value systems confusing.

Instead of writing place values from right to left across the page, as we do, the Maya wrote in columns with units at the bottom. Their zero symbol was a shell. Only three symbols were needed to write any positive integer:

- •    The dot stands for one unit.
- ━    The bar stands for five units.
- (shell)    The shell is the zero placeholder.

| | | | | | | | | |
|---|---|---|---|---|---|---|---|---|
| • | •• | ••• | •••• | ━ | •••• over ━ | •••• over two bars | three bars | •••• over three bars |
| 1 | 2 | 3 | 4 | 5 | 9 | 10 | 15 | 19 |

Numerals were written in columns, with place value increasing from the bottom up. Values from 1 to 19 are entered in the bottom units, or row. With 19, the units row is full. For  20, the Maya put one dot in the 20's place, and a zero symbol in the units place. The next higher place value above 20's was $20 \times 20$, or 400, and so on. For example:

| Examples of Maya Numerals | | | | |
|---|---|---|---|---|
| Place value | | | | |
| 400's ($20^2$) | | | | • |
| 20's ($20^1$) | • | • | •••• | (shell) |
| units ($20^0$) | (shell) | •••• over ━ | • over ━ | •• over ━ |
| Indo-Arabic equivalent | 20 | 29 | 86 | 412 |

*(continued)*

*Algebra Activities from Many Cultures*

# Maya Numerals (continued)

## Questions for Critical Thinking

1. The Maya civilization began about the same time as the Roman civilization, but lasted much longer. Both civilizations developed numerals. Try this addition problem. Write the Maya numerals for each Indo-Arabic numeral, then add both numbers. Do the same problem using Roman numerals. Then create another problem of your own, using Roman numerals and then Maya numerals. Which do you think are easier to add, Roman numerals or Maya numerals?

   (a)  29 + 86

   Maya Numerals: _____

   Roman Numerals: _____

   (b)  Your own addition example:

   Indo-Arabic Numerals: _____

   Maya Numerals: _____

   Roman Numerals: _____

2. Time for the Maya had no beginning, nor did the Maya predict an end. On some Maya monuments, the count of years was written in five-place numerals. (Remember, each place stood for a power of 20, starting with $20^0$.) If there was a single dot • in each place, how many years could be shown in five places?

   _____

   If there was a 19  in each place, how many years could be shown in five places?

   _____

3. Why do you think the Maya and the Aztecs needed such large numbers?

   _____

   _____

   _____

   _____

*Algebra Activities from Many Cultures*

Name _____

Date _____

# Calendars of Central America

One of the most famous Aztec carvings is known as the Calendar Stone. This beautiful stone is in the form of a huge circular disk, 4 m across. It was painted with solar symbols and day signs. The stone reminds us that the Aztecs and other Central American Indians developed very accurate calendars, long before the arrival of Columbus. To develop these calendars, they used the algebraic concept known as the **least common multiple**, or **lcm.**

Calendar Stone

**The least common multiple** was needed to synchronize the calendars used throughout Central America. The calendar for religious events was 260 days long. The solar year of 365 days was used as the civil calendar for daily life. This calendar was adjusted, as needed, to agree with the natural seasons. The cycles of the moon were carefully studied so that the Aztecs could predict eclipses of the sun. The 584-day cycle of the planet Venus was also important in Aztec astronomy.

All these calendars were dated from the same starting day, about 5000 years ago. After many years, the calendars were synchronized again. Then the 260-day, the 365-day, and the 584-day cycles once again started the New Year on the same day. The coincidences of these cycles were very important dates in Central America. They were not thought of as the beginning or the end of the world—just the beginning or end of cycles. The Native Americans of Central America were unique in thinking of time as infinite, without a beginning and without an end. The zero day of the current era was also the final day of the era that was ending.

## SYNCHRONIZING THE CALENDARS OF CENTRAL AMERICA

### Group Project

Some historians are sure that the Aztec and Maya needed multiplication to calculate the time it would take for the different calendars to synchronize. Others disagree and say only addition is needed. Using your calculators, your group can try the calculations for the following examples and make your own decision. Then discuss whether the Aztec and the Maya used multiplication to answer the following questions.

*(continued)*

*Algebra Activities from Many Cultures*

# Calendars of Central America *(continued)*

**Directions:** Fill in the blanks:

1. If the 260-day year and the 365-day year started their New Year on the same day, how long would it take for this to happen again? This period of time is known as the *calendar round* and was very important in Central American astronomy.

   The calendar round would be _____days, or _____ 365-day years. (*Hint:* Find the least common multiple of 260 and 365.)

2. If the 365-day year and the 584-day Venus cycle started on the same day, how long would it take for this to happen again?

   The solar year (365 days) and the Venus year (584 days) start on the same day every _____ days, or _____ solar years.

3. If the 260-day cycle, the 365-day year, and the 584-day Venus cycle all started on the same day, how long would it take for this to happen again?

   The cycles would coincide again in _____ days, or _____ 365-day years.

4. Some Maya monuments in Mexico and Guatemala show very large numbers used for calendar calculations. The Maya also studied a cycle of 819 days and would need large numbers to answer the following question:

   If the 260-day cycle, the 365-day year, the 584-day Venus cycle, and the 819-day cycle all started on the same day, how long would it take for this to happen again ?

   The cycles would coincide again in _____ days.

## Group Discussion

Do you think the above calculations could be done without using multiplication?

© 1997 Beatrice Lumpkin
J. Weston Walch, Publisher

*Algebra Activities from Many Cultures*

# Chinese Number Systems

## Chinese Rod Numerals

### MATERIALS

Reproducible 16

### BACKGROUND

The earliest civilizations in China developed along the banks of three great rivers: the Huang He, or Yellow River; the Chang Jiang, or Yang tze; and the Xi Jiang, or West River. According to legend the Hsin—the first Chinese dynasty, or ruling family—came to power more than 4000 years ago. The first historical period in China began around 1700 B.C.E. under the Shang dynasty. Writing developed during this period. As artisans developed skills in bronze casting and other arts, cities like Anyang developed. Jade carvings were popular, and silkworms were cultivated to provide fine silks for wealthy people. Because silks were so valuable, the way to make it was kept secret by the Chinese for some 3000 years.

### ANSWERS

47 is 三 丌

74 is ⊥ ||||

102 is | ◯ ||

25,613 is || 三 丅 − |||

1.  25 = |||||     104 | ◯ ||||

   +41 三 |        + 97 ⊥ 丌
                       三
   66 ⊥ 丅         201 = ◯ |

   3560 三 ||||| ⊥ ◯

   +4337 三 ||| 三 丌

   7897 ⊥ 丌丌 ⊥ 丌
                三

3.  64,135    丅 三 | 三 |||||

   +57,203    三 丌 = ◯ |||
              三

   121,338  | = | 三 ||| ⊥
                              三

## Signed Numbers with Chinese Rod Numerals

### MATERIALS

toothpicks—some red, some black
Reproducible 17

### PROCEDURE

1. Divide the class into pairs and distribute the handout.

2. Have students proceed as directed on handout, using profit (red) and loss (black) sticks to record each change in Liu Hong's finances.

Name _____

Date _____

# Chinese Rod Numerals

The oldest continuing civilization today is the Chinese. Many important inventions came from China, such as pulp paper, printing, the compass, fireworks, explosives, and seismographs to record earthquakes. Algebra and geometry were also highly developed.

Over 2000 years ago, the Chinese people developed a place-value system of numerals based on 10. A circle was used for the zero placeholder. The numerals we use today, known as Indo-Arabic, use the same principles. The Chinese numerals are called *rod numerals* because they were formed with small bamboo rods. The Chinese arranged them in columns and moved the rods for addition, something like an abacus. We believe that rod numerals were the inspiration for the Chinese abacus.

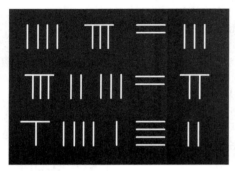

Positional value in the Chinese system was shown by alternating vertical and horizontal numerals. Vertical numerals were used for units, horizontal for tens, vertical for hundreds, horizontal for thousands, etc. Their numerals for one to nine were:

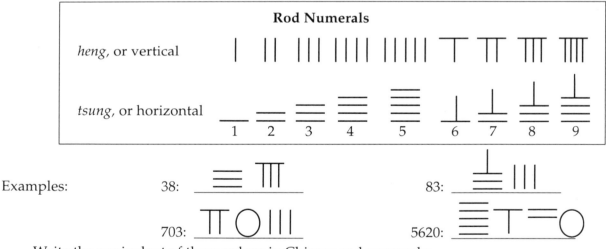

Examples:    38: _____    83: _____

703: _____    5620: _____

Write the equivalent of these values in Chinese rod numerals:

47 _____    74 _____    102 _____    25,613 _____

*(continued)*

J. Weston Walch, Publisher

*Algebra Activities from Many Cultures*

# Chinese Rod Numerals *(continued)*

## ADDITION

Line up the rods in columns, according to place value. Just count the rods, remembering that for 6, 7, 8, and 9, the rod at right angles to the other rod has the value, 5. For example, add ⊤⊤ and ⊤⊤⊤. The two top bars add to 10. There are || + ||| = ||||| vertical bars. The sum is | ||||| .

## CHINESE ROD NUMERALS AND THE ABACUS

**Directions:** Work with a partner on the following problems.

1. Write these numerals as Chinese Rod numerals. Then add in columns, according to place value:

   25 _____       104 _____       3560 _____

   + _____       + _____       + _____

   41 _____        97 _____       4337 _____


   _____       _____       _____

2. Probably you added the numerals starting at the right, with units, and working to the left. Repeat the additions above but this time start at the left, with the highest value.

   25 _____       104 _____       3560 _____

   + _____       + _____       + _____

   41 _____        97 _____       4337 _____


   _____       _____       _____

3. Challenge: Use Chinese rod numerals to add 64,135 + 57,203 in the space below.

37

*Algebra Activities from Many Cultures*

# Signed Numbers with Chinese Rod Numerals

Some 2000 years ago, Chinese bookkeepers found an easy way to work with profits and losses. They discovered the rules for addition and subtraction of positive and negative numbers. They used small red sticks for profits (positive) and small black sticks for losses (negative). The basic idea was that one red (positive) and one black (negative) wiped each other out to give zero.

**Rod Numerals**

| | | | | | | | | | |
|---|---|---|---|---|---|---|---|---|---|
| *heng*, or vertical | ❘ | ❘❘ | ❘❘❘ | ❘❘❘❘ | ❘❘❘❘❘ | ⊤ | ⊤⊤ | ⊤⊤⊤ | ⊤⊤⊤⊤ |
| *tsung*, or horizontal | — | = | ☰ | ☰ | ☰ | ⊥ | ⊥ | ⊥ | ⊥ |
| | 1 | 2 | 3 | 4 | 5 | 6 | 7 | 8 | 9 |

## Project

With a partner, follow this scenario. Use one toothpick to stand for a piece of jade. Model each step with red and black toothpicks. Then make up your own story that you can demonstrate to the class.

1. Liu Hong, a merchant, started with 6 pieces of jade. Then he sold some silk cloth and made a profit of 2 pieces of jade. 6 + 2 = 8

2. In a bad business deal, Liu Hong lost 1 piece of jade. 8 – 1 = 7

3. Then he sent a young man to get some cloth equal to the value of 10 pieces of jade. The river flooded, the cloth was lost, and the young man barely escaped. Liu Hong ended up in debt. 7 – 10 = –3

4. His troubles accumulated. Already in debt for 3 pieces, Liu Hong had to pay the young man 2 pieces of jade for his work. –3 – 2 = –5

**Color code**
(positive)   (negative)
red     black

⊤ and ❘❘ = ⊤⊤⊤

⊤⊤⊤ and ❘ = ⊤⊤

⊤⊤ and —O = ❘❘❘

❘❘❘ and ❘❘ = ❘❘❘❘❘

*(continued)*

*Algebra Activities from Many Cultures*

# Signed Numbers with
# Chinese Rod Numerals *(continued)*

5. The young man to whom Liu Hong owed 2 pieces of jade wanted to marry Liu's daughter. So he told Liu Hong to forget (take away) the 2-piece debt. Taking away, or subtracting –2 was like adding +2.  –5 – –2 = –3

   $$||||| \text{ and } || = |||$$

6. Happy ending! Liu Hong worked very hard and had a profit of 5 pieces of jade. He was back in the red again! –3 + 5 = 2

   $$||| \text{ and } ||||| = ||$$

Translate the color of the toothpicks to "sign" and the number of toothpicks to "absolute value," and you get these two rules:

> • *Rule 1:* When adding numbers with the **same sign**, **add** their **absolute values** and **keep** the **sign**.

> • *Rule 2:* When adding numbers with **opposite signs**, take the **difference** in their **absolute values** and use the **sign of the larger absolute value**.

7. Now make up your own profit-and-loss story to model with colored toothpicks.

*Algebra Activities from Many Cultures*

# Indian Number Systems

## BACKGROUND

Thousands of years ago, in the northwestern sector of the Indian subcontinent, the flooding Indus River deposited silt on the lands it crossed between the mountains and the sea. Early farmers grew many crops in the fertile alluvial soil—so many that, by 2500 B.C.E., cities like Mohenjo-Daro and Harappa came to be built. The streets of these cities were planned. The buildings were made of bricks, shaped to a regular size and baked in wood-fired ovens. Most houses had several rooms, a courtyard, a well, and a bathroom. A system of brick sewers kept the cities clean and healthful.

The people of the Indus Valley were the first to make cloth from cotton. They used the wheel to make pots and traded with people as far away as Persia and Mesopotamia. A standard system of weights and measures was developed, as well as a system of writing, using pictograms. Some progress is being made in deciphering the writing system.

## Indian Numerals: From Harappan to Modern

### MATERIALS

Reproducible 18

### PROCEDURE

1. Distribute the handout.

2. Ask students to study the numerals.

3. Have students answer the questions.

## ANSWERS

1. Answers will vary
2. Answers will vary
3. Answers will vary.
4. (a) 850

   (b) DCCCL

## DISCUSSION

Have students discuss the following question: Do you think the Vedic and Harappan were related?

## EXTENSION ACTIVITY

Divide the class into groups. Give each group the following prompt: Suppose you were in a market. You do not know the language spoken there and have no way to write numerals. With hand signals only, can you represent numbers so others in your group will know what number you are showing?

When all groups have developed a system of hand signals, combine groups and see if different groups can understand each others' signals.

## Indian History: A Puzzle

### MATERIALS

Reproducible 19

### PROCEDURE

1. Distribute the handout.

2. Have students study the table comparing Harappan and Vedic weights.

3. Tell students to answer the questions.

### ANSWERS

1. Yes
2. $y = 18x$
3. $z = (80/9)y$
4. $z = (80/9)18x$, $z = 160x$

# Indian Numerals

## From Harappan to Modern

The great subcontinent of India is home to a large part of the world's population. It is also the home of one of the world's oldest civilizations. Great buildings and baths that are over 4000 years old still stand at cities with names like Mohenjo-Daro and Harappa. The Harappans cultivated cotton, domesticated the chicken, and may have invented the game of chess. They seem to have standardized many things: brick sizes, weights and measures, and building plans. These standards are part of the evidence that links the Harappan civilization with modern village India.

The Harappans had a class of scribes in charge of standard measures and the distributing of supplies. The script they used is still largely untranslated, even after years of modern research. Recently, the Harappan language was identified as one of the Dravidian languages, a family of languages spoken in India today.

Harappan numerals have been deciphered. They show that Harappans used tally marks for 1 through 7. For 8, they used a double sun; for 9, a foundation post. Symbols for 10 and 100 are also known, which suggests that an original base-8 system was later modified to a base-10 system of numbers.

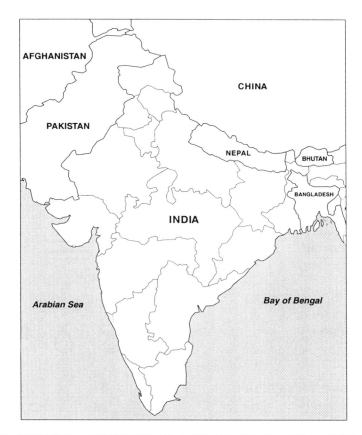

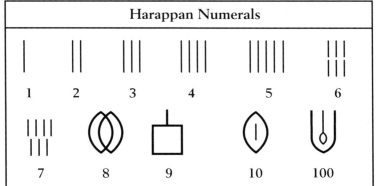

Harappan Numerals

(after Walter Fairservis, Jr.)

*(continued)*

# Indian Numerals (continued)

About 1500 B.C.E., a Sanskrit-speaking people entered India from the north. There was a mingling of cultures in India and extensive trade with China, Mesopotamia, and Africa. There was also a rapid growth in all of the sciences, especially astronomy. Astronomers had to work with large numbers and needed an efficient system of numerals. A process began in India that ended with the invention of the numerals we use today.

In India, mathematicians took the best of the old ideas and made their own giant step forward. By the year 600, Indians had invented ciphers for numbers 1 to 9 and used them in a place value system. Soon after, a small circle was employed as a zero placeholder. These are the numerals we use today, called the Indo-Arabic numerals. Islamic mathematicians expanded the system to include decimal fractions. They also introduced the numerals to Europe where Indo-Arabic numerals gradually replaced Roman numerals.

## STAGES IN DEVELOPMENT OF INDIAN NUMERALS

The table below shows three stages in the development of Indian numerals.

| Brahmi Numerals | | | | | | | | | | |
| --- | --- | --- | --- | --- | --- | --- | --- | --- | --- | --- |
| Gwalior Numerals | | | | | | | | | | |
| Modern Indo-Arabic Numerals | 1 | 2 | 3 | 4 | 5 | 6 | 7 | 8 | 9 | 0 |

## Questions for Critical Thinking

1. Why do you think Harappans standardized brick sizes?

_____

_____

_____

_____

*(continued)*

# Indian Numerals *(continued)*

2. Why do you think Harappans standardized weights and scales for length?

_____

_____

_____

_____

3. Refer to the chart of Brahmi numerals, Gwalior numerals, and modern numerals. Select some numerals that changed the most. Show possible intermediate stages for the changes.

| Early numeral | Intermediate stages | Modern numeral |
|---|---|---|
| _____ | _____ | _____ |
| _____ | _____ | _____ |
| _____ | _____ | _____ |
| _____ | _____ | _____ |

4. Multiply 25 × 34 using

   (a) Indo-Arabic numerals

   (b) Roman numerals

## Group Discussion

What are the advantages of Indo-Arabic numerals compared to Roman numerals?

# Indian History

### A Puzzle

Archaeologists are fascinated by the Harappan civilization of India dating back to 2500 B.C.E. These ancient people of India left imposing buildings, weights and measures, and a script that is still being deciphered. Who were they? And are the modern people of India their descendants?

Indian scientists are using mathematics to help solve this puzzle. They are exploring possible connections between Harappan weights and Vedic weights. The Vedic civilization is considered the parent of modern India and appeared hundreds of years after the Harappan. The Vedic unit of weight for precious metals was the gunja seed, similar to the grain in English measure. If the Harappan and Vedic systems of weights are related, that would show continuity from the earlier to the later civilization. The following table compares the two systems of weights. Values have been rounded off.

| Comparison of Harappan and Vedic Weights* | | |
|---|---|---|
| Harappan Weights | | Vedic Weights |
| Relative Size | Grams | Number of Gunja Seeds |
| $x$ | $y$ | $z$ |
| 0.05 | 0.9 | 8 |
| 0.1 | 1.8 | 16 |
| 0.2 | 3.6 | 32 |
| 0.5 | 9.0 | 80 |
| 1 | 18.0 | 160 |
| 2 | 36.0 | 320 |

1. On a piece of graph paper, plot the number of grams *vs.* relative size. Select suitable range values. Is this a linear function?

2. Write an equation in the form of $y = f(x)$ to represent this graph.

_____

3. Write an equation for $z$, the number of gunja seeds, as a function of $y$, or $z = g(y)$.

_____

4. Use composition of functions $g[f(x)]$ to write $z$ as a function of $x$.

_____

© 1997 Beatrice Lumpkin
J. Weston Walch, Publisher

*Algebra Activities from Many Cultures*

# Fractions from Africa and Asia

## Take $\frac{1}{2}$ to Infinity: Horus Eye Fractions

### MATERIALS

Reproducible 20

### ANSWERS

0.25     0.125     0.0625
0.03125     0.015625

1. $(0.5)^{10} = .000976562$

2. $(0.5)^{20} = .000000953$

3. $(0.5)^{30} = 9.3 \times 10^{-10}$

4. $(0.5)^{40} = 9.09 \times 10^{-13}$

5. $(0.5)^{50} = 8.88 \times 10^{-16}$

6. $[(0.5)^{50}]^2 = 7.89 \times 10^{-31}$

7. $[(0.5)^{100}]^2 = 6.223 \times 10^{-61}$

8. $[(0.5)^{200}]^2 = 0$

### Group Discussion

1. Answers will vary

2. Decreasing

3. Increasing

4. $(0.5)^{30}$

## Modern Fractions from North Africa

### MATERIALS

Reproducible 21

### ANSWERS

1. $\frac{4}{9}$  5. $a^2b$

2. $\frac{1}{3}$  6. $\dfrac{u^2 + v^2}{uv}$

3. $\frac{x}{y}$  7. $\dfrac{x^4 + y^4}{x^2 y^2}$

4. $a^2b$  8. $\frac{34}{15}$

9. $\dfrac{x^2 + y^2}{xy} = \dfrac{x^2}{xy} + \dfrac{y^2}{xy} = \dfrac{x}{y} + \dfrac{y}{x}$

## Equations with Fractions from Egypt, India, and China

### MATERIALS

Reproducible 22

### ANSWERS

1. $\dfrac{9}{30}$ or $\dfrac{1}{5} + \dfrac{1}{10}$

2. $\dfrac{49}{360}$ or $\dfrac{1}{9} + \dfrac{1}{40}$

### FRACTIONS FROM INDIA

$\dfrac{1}{14}$ day; $\dfrac{2}{14}, \dfrac{3}{14}, \dfrac{4}{14}, \dfrac{5}{14}$

### FRACTIONS FROM CHINA

$\dfrac{15}{74}$ day

# Take $\frac{1}{2}$ to Infinity

## Horus Eye Fractions

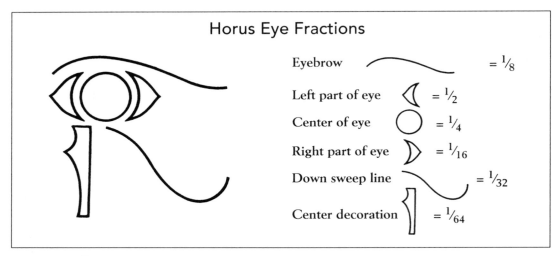

Horus Eye Fractions

Eyebrow      $= \frac{1}{8}$

Left part of eye      $= \frac{1}{2}$

Center of eye      $= \frac{1}{4}$

Right part of eye      $= \frac{1}{16}$

Down sweep line      $= \frac{1}{32}$

Center decoration      $= \frac{1}{64}$

Most likely, $\frac{1}{2}$ was the first fraction used by people. A very old Egyptian papyrus says, "Take $\frac{1}{2}$ to infinity . . ." The rest cannot be read because the papyrus is torn. Although we cannot read the rest of that torn papyrus, we do know that the ancient Egyptian mathematicians were skilled in operations with fractions.

Fractions were invented early in history because they were needed to carry on trade and to build monuments such as pyramids. Fractions were an important part of the ancient Egyptian story about the trinity of Osiris, Isis, and Horus.

According to the story, Horus was the child of Osiris, the god of grain, and Isis, the mother god. He was born after his father, Osiris, had been murdered by his jealous brother, Seth. Seth cut up the body of Osiris and scattered the pieces all over Egypt. But Isis, who was a magician, put the pieces together again. Still, Osiris could not return to earth because one piece was missing. Instead, Osiris became the ruler of the underworld.

When Horus grew up, he fought with Seth to avenge his father. It was a terrible fight. Seth knocked out Horus's eye. The eye fell to the ground and broke in half. Then one half bounced up, fell, and broke in half again. That $\frac{1}{4}$ of the eye bounced and broke in half again. Then $\frac{1}{8}$ of the eye broke into $\frac{1}{16}$, $\frac{1}{32}$, and last, $\frac{1}{64}$.

Isis, the magician, picked up the pieces and put her son's eye back together again. She had $\frac{1}{2}$, $\frac{1}{4}$, $\frac{1}{8}$, $\frac{1}{32}$ and $\frac{1}{64}$. The missing $\frac{1}{64}$ was supplied by Djewuti, the god of wisdom. Since that day, it is said, the Horus eye fractions were held sacred by the ancient Egyptians.

*(continued)*

*Algebra Activities from Many Cultures*

# Take $\frac{1}{2}$ to Infinity *(continued)*

## EXPLORATION

What happens if you keep taking $\frac{1}{2}$ of $\frac{1}{2}$ of $\frac{1}{2}$? In algebraic terms, what happens to the value of $(\frac{1}{2})^n$ as $n$ increases without bound?

Enter 0.5, the decimal equivalent of $\frac{1}{2}$, on your calculator. Start to multiply $0.5 \times 0.5$ until you get the decimal equivalents of the Horus Eye fractions down to $\frac{1}{64}$.

$\frac{1}{2} = (0.5)$ $\qquad$ $\frac{1}{4} = (0.5)^2 =$ _____ $\qquad$ $\frac{1}{8} = (0.5)^3 =$ _____

$\frac{1}{16} = (0.5)^4 =$ _____ $\qquad$ $\frac{1}{32} = (0.5)^5 =$ _____ $\qquad$ $\frac{1}{64} = (0.5)^6 =$ _____

Continue to take $\frac{1}{2}$ by multiplying by 0.5. Make a record of every 10 operations. With a calculator you can do that quickly by finding $(0.5)^{10}$, $(0.5)^{20}$, $(0.5)^{30}$, $(0.5)^{40}$, $(0.5)^{50}$. Then you might want to move more rapidly by squaring your last results: $[(0.5)^{50}]^2$, $[(0.5)^{100}]^2$, $[(0.5)^{200}]^2$.

1. $(0.5)^{10} =$ _____

2. $(0.5)^{20} =$ _____

3. $(0.5)^{30} =$ _____

4. $(0.5)^{40} =$ _____

5. $(0.5)^{50} =$ _____

6. $[(0.5)^{50}]^2 =$ _____

7. $[(0.5)^{100}]^2 =$ _____

8. $[(0.5)^{200}]^2 =$ _____

## Group Discussion

1. Are any of your calculator readings 0? If so, do you think that the reading is correct?

   _____

2. Each time you take $\frac{1}{2}$, is your value increasing or decreasing?

   _____

3. Suppose you started with a negative value, say –2. Each time you take $\frac{1}{2}$, is your value increasing or decreasing? Check your answers on a number line.

   _____

4. Which is smaller, $(0.5)^{20}$ or $(0.5)^{30}$ ? _____

*Algebra Activities from Many Cultures*

# Modern Fractions from North Africa

## ABU KAMIL'S RULE FOR SIMPLIFYING FRACTIONS

Abu Kamil, called the Egyptian calculator, was born in 850 B.C.E. He proved the basic rules for algebraic fractions that we use today. For example, he wrote:

> For every number which one divides by another, then, the quotient is equal to the square of the dividend divided by the product of the dividend and divisor.

Today, we write Abu Kamil's rule as:

| **Rule 1** | $\dfrac{a}{b} = \dfrac{a^2}{ab}$, or $\dfrac{a^2}{ab} = \dfrac{a}{b}$ |

Isn't that easier to read than all the words Abu Kamil had to use? For thousands of years, mathematicians have been developing easier ways to do algebra. We use an extension of that rule today anytime we "cancel" to simplify a fraction. For example:

$$\frac{3}{4} = \frac{3 \times 3}{3 \times 4} = \frac{9}{12} \text{ or } \frac{9}{12} = \frac{3 \times 3}{3 \times 4} = \frac{3}{4}$$

Sometime after Abu Kamil, Islamic mathematicians in Spain and North Africa began to use the modern fraction bar. Instead of writing "three fourths," they were the first to write the fraction as ³⁄₄.

A young Italian student known as Fibonacci studied mathematics in North Africa about the year 1200. He introduced North African mathematics to Europe, including the idea of using a fraction bar.

Abu Kamil also proved another useful rule.

| **Rule 2** | $\dfrac{x}{y} + \dfrac{y}{x} = \dfrac{x^2 + y^2}{xy}$ |

Extend Abu Kamil's Rule 1 to simplify (reduce) the following fractions:

1. $\dfrac{16}{36} = $ _____

2. $\dfrac{22}{66} = $ _____

3. $\dfrac{x^2}{xy} = $ _____

4. $\dfrac{a^3 b^2}{ab} = $ _____

5. $\dfrac{a^3 b^2 c}{abc} = $ _____

Use Abu Kamil's Rule 2 to combine the following fractions:

6. $\dfrac{u}{v} + \dfrac{v}{u} = $ _____

7. $\dfrac{x^2}{y^2} + \dfrac{y^2}{x^2} = $ _____

8. $\dfrac{3}{5} + \dfrac{5}{3} = $ _____

9. Show that Abu Kamil's Rule 2 is correct by combining and simplifying:

   $\dfrac{x}{y} + \dfrac{y}{x}$  _____

*Algebra Activities from Many Cultures*

Name _____

Date _____

# Equations with Fractions
# from Egypt, India, and China

Equations from ancient Egypt were used to solve problems that arose in everyday life. Naturally, fractions appeared in these equations. Notice that except for $\frac{2}{3}$ and sometimes $\frac{3}{4}$, Egyptians used unit fractions—fractions with a numerator of 1. So $\frac{2}{5}$ would be written as $\frac{1}{3} + \frac{1}{15}$. The scribes had special tables to make their work easier.

*Example:* What must be added to $\frac{2}{3} + \frac{1}{15}$ to get 1? The modern equation form would be: $x + \frac{2}{3} + \frac{1}{15} = 1$.

The Egyptians selected 15 as the common denominator. Then they thought of 1 as divided into 15 equal parts. To get a whole unit they needed 15 parts. How many parts did they have? They showed:

$\frac{2}{3}$ of 15 is 10, and $\frac{1}{15}$ of 15 is 1. The sum of the parts is 10 + 1 = 11 parts.

To get 15 parts, 4 more parts were needed. We would write the answer as $\frac{4}{15}$.

They wrote: $\frac{1}{5}$ of 15 is 3; $\frac{1}{15}$ of 15 is 1. Their answer was $\frac{1}{5} + \frac{1}{15}$.

The proof was always shown. 10 + 3 + 1 + 1 = 15 (understood to be fifteenths).

**Directions:** Solve these "completion" problems from Ahmose's papyrus. Use both the Egyptian method and the modern method.

1. Complete $\frac{2}{3} + \frac{1}{30}$ to get 1. _____

2. Complete $\frac{1}{4} + \frac{1}{8} + \frac{1}{10} + \frac{1}{30} + \frac{1}{45}$ to get $\frac{2}{3}$. _____

## AN EQUATION WITH FRACTIONS FROM INDIA

The famous ninth-century Indian mathematician Mahavira posed this problem:
A pool will be filled by water from four pipes. Each pipe, by itself, could fill the pool in different parts of a day: $\frac{1}{2}$, $\frac{1}{3}$, $\frac{1}{4}$, and $\frac{1}{5}$ day. How long would it take to fill the pool using all four pipes? What part of the pool would each pipe fill?

## AN EQUATION WITH FRACTIONS FROM CHINA

An even earlier Chinese example, similar to Mahavira's problem, has five pipes:
Five pipes enter a reservoir. The times to fill the reservoir by one pipe alone are: $\frac{1}{3}$, 1, $2\frac{1}{2}$, 3, and 5 days. If the pipes are all open, in how many days will the reservoir fill?

*Algebra Activities from Many Cultures*

# First-Degree Equations

## The Egyptian Method of Solving Equations

### MATERIALS

Reproducible 23

### PROCEDURE

1. Distribute the handout.
2. Have students proceed as directed.

### ANSWERS

1. 1858 – –1650 = 3508 years
2. 21
3. $16\frac{5}{8}$
4. $10\frac{2}{3}$
5. $\frac{3}{10}$ hekat or 96 ro

## More Equations from Africa and Asia

### MATERIALS

Reproducible 24

### PROCEDURE

1. Distribute the handout.
2. Have students proceed as directed.

### ANSWERS

1. 14.289

2. $13\frac{1}{2}$

3. $(\frac{12}{11})(\frac{8}{7})x = 1$ mana = 60 shekels

   $x = \frac{77}{96}$ mana = $48\frac{1}{8}$ shekels

4. Answers will vary.

5. $x$ = original amount

   $(\frac{6}{7})(\frac{4}{5})(\frac{2x}{3}) = 5,$

   $\frac{48x}{105} = 5$

   answer: 10.9375 measures

## Equations from Mexico

### MATERIALS

Reproducible 25

### PROCEDURE

1. Distribute the handout.
2. Have students proceed as directed.

### ANSWERS

1. 1189 pesos and 4 tomines
2. $416 = .26x$; $x$ = 1600 pesos, 1184 pesos due
3. $.30x = 200$; $x = 666\frac{2}{3}$ reales
4. (a) 6 pesos; $9x = 34 + 20$

   (b) purchase of 1 vara at the regular price

## Equations from Guatemala

### MATERIALS

Reproducible 26

### PROCEDURE

1. Distribute the handout.

2. Have students proceed as directed.

### ANSWERS

1. 60

2. 300

3. 96

#### Questions for Critical Thinking

True for all numbers. $(\frac{1}{2} + \frac{1}{3} + \frac{1}{4} - \frac{1}{12})x = x$ is an identity.

4. $10\frac{2}{3}, 21\frac{1}{3}$

5. $x + \frac{x}{2} + 9 + \frac{x}{4} - 4 = 110, x = 60$

6. $10x + 8 = 18x - 22, x = 3\frac{3}{4}$

## Making Models for Algebra

### MATERIALS

Reproducible 27

### PROCEDURE

1. Distribute the handout.

2. Have students proceed as directed.

### ANSWERS

1. $12x$

2.

## Slopes of the Pyramids in Africa and America

### MATERIALS

Reproducible 28

### PROCEDURE

1. Distribute the handout.

2. Have students proceed as directed.

### ANSWERS

1. $\frac{180}{250} = 0.72$

2. $\frac{250}{180} = 1.39$

3. $93\frac{1}{3}$ cubits

4. 0.25

5. Pyramid in question 1 has the larger *seked*, pyramid in question 4 has the larger *slope*.

#### Critical Thinking

1. (a) 1.08

   (b) 1.28

2. Answers will vary. There is a temple on top of the Castillo, so stairways were needed to get to the temple.

# The Egyptian Method of Solving Equations

Almost 4,000 years ago, a mathematics textbook was written in ancient Egypt. In addition to present-day Egypt, the ancient Egyptian empire included much of the Sudan, parts of Ethiopia, and Syria-Palestine. The textbook was copied on papyrus—paper made by layering strips of papyrus reed—by the scribe Ah'mose about 1650 B.C.E. After thousands of years, most papyrus books perished. Ah'mose's book survived. It was bought in 1858 by a Scottish tourist named Henry A. Rhind.

There are many equations in the Ah'mose papyrus. They were solved by an experimental method that used proportional thinking. Ah'mose set up an equation and fed in any convenient number, a "false" value. It was not expected to work. But the error that resulted led to a proportional correction which produced the correct solution.

---

**Ah'mose example 26:**

A heap, and 1/4 of a heap are added together. The sum is 15. How big is the heap?

---

The ancient Egyptians used the word for heap the way we use the symbol x, to stand for an unknown quantity. The modern way of writing Ah'mose's equation is:

$$x + (\tfrac{1}{4})x = 15$$

**The Egyptian solution:**

Step 1. Try any convenient value, such as $x = 4$.

Step 2. Substitute $x = 4$ in the equation.

$$4 + (\tfrac{1}{4})4 = 5$$

Does $4 + 1 = 15$? No, it does not, $5 = 15$ is false!

Step 3. To get 15 from 5, multiply by 3. A correction factor of 3 is needed.

Step 4. Multiply the false value, $x = 4$, by the correction factor, 3.

The solution is $x = 4 \times 3$; $x = 12$.

Step 5. Egyptian mathematicians always completed a problem by showing the proof:

$$x + (\tfrac{1}{4})x = 15$$

$$12 + (\tfrac{1}{4})12 = 15$$

$$15 = 15$$

The proportion used was the correct value/false value = $\dfrac{15}{5}$; $\dfrac{x}{4} = \dfrac{15}{5}$.

*(continued)*

# The Egyptian Method of Solving Equations *(continued)*

⋈◁⋈◁⋈◁⋈◁⋈◁⋈◁⋈◁⋈◁⋈◁⋈◁⋈◁⋈◁⋈◁⋈◁⋈◁⋈

## Questions for Critical Thinking

1. How old was the Ah'mose Papyrus when Rhind bought it?

   _____

2. Use the Egyptian method of "false position" to solve this puzzle. Show the proof.

   > A heap, and $\frac{1}{7}$ of a heap are added together. The sum is 24. How big is the heap?

3. Most Ah'mose quantity problems involved fractions. Fractions didn't bother the Egyptians because they had tables to simplify their work  Use Egyptian "false position" to solve this puzzle:

   > A heap, and $\frac{1}{7}$ of a heap are added together. The sum is 19. How big is the heap?

4. Another Ah'mose example, no. 25,  asked:

   > A heap, and $\frac{1}{2}$ of a heap are added together. The sum is 16. How big is the heap?

5. Ah'mose example no. 35:

   > Find the size of a cup which filled $3\frac{1}{3}$ times with wheat provides 1 hekat of wheat. (There are 320 ro in 1 hekat measure.)

# More Equations from Africa and Asia

**Directions:** Write an equation for each situation. Solve and check.

1. **Egypt:** Ah'mose example 31. (Let x = the unknown quantity, or heap.)

   > The sum of a heap, $\frac{2}{3}$ of the heap, $\frac{1}{2}$ of the heap, and $\frac{1}{7}$ of the heap is 33. How big is the heap?

   _____

2. **Egypt:** Ah'mose example 29.

   > A heap and $\frac{2}{3}$ of a heap are added together, and $\frac{1}{3}$ of the sum is added. Finally, $\frac{1}{3}$ of this last sum is 10. How big was the heap?

   _____

3. **Old Babylonia:**

   > I found a stone but did not weigh it. To that unknown weight I added $\frac{1}{7}$ more of it, then added to it $\frac{1}{11}$ more of the new total. Now it weighed 1 ma-na. What was the original weight of the stone? Note: There are 60 shekels to 1 ma-na.

   _____

4. Refer to the Babylonian example in question 3. In real life, can you add exactly $\frac{1}{7}$ of a weight without knowing the size of the weight? Was this a practical problem? Why or why not?

   _____

   _____

   _____

5. **An ancient Chinese puzzle.**

   > A woman carrying rice in old China passes 3 customs stations and must pay a tariff in rice. The first station collects $\frac{1}{3}$ of her rice, the second takes $\frac{1}{5}$ of what was left, and the third $\frac{1}{7}$ of what remains. Only 5 measures of rice are left for the woman. How many did she start with?

   _____

*Algebra Activities from Many Cultures*

# Equations from Mexico

The first algebra book produced in the Americas was written by Juan Diez and was printed in Mexico City in 1556. It is titled *El Sumario Compendioso*. Examples from this book tell something about Spanish trade in Mexico at that time. Much of the trade dealt in luxuries: silver, gold, and velvet cloth. The trade in silver and gold was heavily taxed by the Spanish king. The following examples are from the book by Juan Diez.

**Directions:** Write an equation for each situation. Solve and check.

**Example 1.** The tax rate in 16th century Mexico was 25% on silver currency, plus a 1% service fee. Find the tax and fee on 4575 silver pesos.

(For fractions of a peso, use coins called tomines. There were 8 tomines to 1 peso. Tomine means eight in Arabic.)

_____

**Example 2.** "Rule for collecting what is due from his majesty." Evidently merchants had trouble getting back the correct amount of gold from the king's assessor. Diez helped the merchants calculate what was due them after they brought their gold to the tax assessor.

Gold was taxed a total of 26% by the king's assessor. A gold merchant paid a fee of 416 pesos. How much gold had he brought to the assessor? What was "due from his Majesty?"

_____

**Example 3.** The merchants' commission on the sale of gold was 30%, payable in coins called reales. If a commission on a sale of gold was 200 reales, what was the value of the gold?

_____

**Example 4.** I needed 10 varas of velvet. There was this great sale but it had a limit of 9 varas to a customer (1 vara was a little less than a yard). So I paid 34 pesos for 9 varas at the sale price. I saved 20 pesos. Then I bought 1 vara at the regular price.

(a) What was the regular price per vara?

_____

(b) What information was not needed?

_____

_____

_____

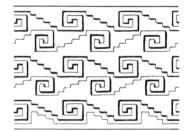

*Algebra Activities from Many Cultures*

# Equations from Guatemala

In 1732, an algebra book written by Juan Joseph de Padilla was published in Guatemala City. It was titled *Noticia Breve de Todas las Reglas Mas Principales de la Arithmetica Practica*. Solve the following problems from de Padilla's book.

**Directions:** Write an equation for each situation. Solve and check.

1. Find a number which, when added to its half, its third, and its fourth, gives a sum of 125.

   _____

2. Find a number which, when its half and its third are subtracted from the number, then its tenth is added, the result is 80.

   _____

3. Find a number whose half, third and fourth, minus its twelfth, give a sum of 96.

   _____

▰◁▰◁▰◁▰◁▰◁▰◁▰◁▰◁▰◁▰◁▰◁▰◁▰◁▰◁▰◁▰◁▰◁

## Questions for Critical Thinking

Is it true for any number that its half, third and fourth, minus its twelfth, gives the number itself?

   _____

4. Find 2 numbers, one twice the size of the other. Multiply the smaller by 30 and the larger by 60. The sum of these products is 1600.

   _____

5. Add to a number half of it and 9 more, and 4 less than 1/4 of it. The sum is 110. What is the number?

   _____

6. Find a number that multiplied by 10, then added to 8, gives a result equal to multiplying the number by 18, then subtracting 22.

   _____

Name _____

Date _____

# Making Models for Algebra

Al-Khwarizmi was a great mathematician, astronomer, and geographer from Central Asia, a longtime center of mathematics. He wrote in Arabic—which was not his native language—because Arabic was the language of science during the Middle Ages. For thousands of years, the subject of algebra had been studied in Africa and Asia, but it was new to 9th century Europe. Al-Khwarizmi wrote a book, *Al-jabr w'al-muqabala*, that had so much influence in Europe that Europeans named the subject after the first two words of the book's title, *Al-jabr*. *Al-jabr* became known as "algebra." The word "algorithm" is a rewriting of the name al-Khwarizmi. An algorithm is a procedure used in mathematics.

About 50 years after al-Khwarizmi, an even more advanced algebra was developed by Abu Kamil, known as the "Egyptian Calculator." Abu Kamil used many diagrams to show that his solutions were correct. For example, to show the multiplication of $3x$ by 6, Abu-Kamil drew the diagram shown below:

**Models by Abu Kamil**

$(3x)(6) = 18x$ $\qquad\qquad\qquad$ $(x + 10)(x + 10) = x^2 + 20x + 100$

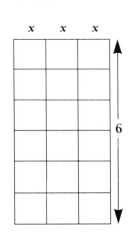

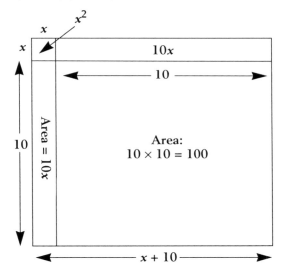

You can make algebraic models, just as Abu Kamil did. Use algebra tiles or cut out rectangles of colored graph paper. The models also give good insight into the meaning of algebraic expressions.

## GEOMETRIC MODELS FOR ALGEBRA

Use Abu Kamil's method to make a geometric model for the following algebraic expressions:

1. $3(4x)$

2. $(x + 5)(x + 5) = x^2 + 10x + 25$

*Algebra Activities from Many Cultures*

# Slopes of the Pyramids
# in Africa and America

   Slope is one of the oldest ideas in mathematics. The slope ratio had been used in Egypt years before the first pyramid was built in 2700 B.C.E. It was natural that the early African engineers had to consider slope, the ratio of height to the setback of the wall, in order to build huge stone monuments. A pyramid in Egypt, called the "bent" pyramid, looks peculiar because the slope was suddenly changed. Either the slope was too high and the wall collapsed, or the pharaoh died unexpectedly and they had to finish the pyramid in a hurry. When a line's slope is not constant, the line is no longer straight.

   Egyptians used the ratio of run to rise, actually the inverse of today's slope. It was called the "seked" and was a standard topic in ancient Egyptian mathematics classes. Here are some examples from one of the oldest mathematics textbooks, the Ah'mose Papyrus.

1.  If a pyramid is 250 cubits high and the side of its square base is 360 cubits long, what is its seked? Hint: To find the run, take ½ the length of the square base.

   _____

2.  What is the slope of the pyramid in question 1?

   _____

3.  If the seked of a pyramid is 5 palms 1 finger per cubit and the side of its base 140 cubits, what is its height? (There are 7 palms to 1 cubit, and 4 fingers to 1 palm.)

   _____

4.  If a small pyramid is 30 cubits high and the side of its square base is 15 cubits long, what is its seked?

   _____

5.  Which slope is greater, that of the pyramid in question 1 or the small pyramid in question 4?

   _____

*(continued)*

*Algebra Activities from Many Cultures*

# Slopes of the Pyramids
## in Africa and America *(continued)*

Some Central American pyramids of the Maya, the Toltecs, and the Aztecs are as massive as the African pyramids. But the pyramids of Central America are somewhat different in concept. African pyramids rise to a point. Most Mexican pyramids have stairways that lead to a temple on top. Some stairways are so steep that tourists prefer to face the top and look up, even when going down the stairs!

How steep are these pyramids? It is interesting to compare the slopes.

### Questions for Critical Thinking

1. Compare the slopes of Khufu's pyramid near Cairo, and the Castillo at Chichen Itza in Mexico.

   (a) The stairway at the Castillo is parallel to the side of the pyramid. Therefore the stairway and the pyramid have the same slope. If the height (rise) of the stairway is 27 m, and the run is 25 m, what is the slope?

   _____

   (b) The height of Khufu's pyramid is 482 ft, or 144.6 m. Each side of the square base is 756 ft, or 226.8 m. What is the slope? Hint: First find the run.

   _____

2. Why do you suppose Mexican pyramids have stairways but Egyptian pyramids do not? Consider slope, shape, possible different uses of the pyramids, and other factors.

   _____

   _____

   _____

   _____

   _____

   _____

*Algebra Activities from Many Cultures*

# Systems of Equations

## Systems of Equations from Guatemala

### MATERIALS

Reproducible 29

### PROCEDURE

1. Distribute the handout.

2. Have students proceed as directed.

### ANSWERS

1. initially, 3000 Moors to 500 Castilians; later, 3600 to 900

2. $y = x + 30$, $y = 3(2)x$; $x = 60$ varas, $y = 90$ varas or 49.8 m, 74.7 m

3. $x + y + z = 90$; $y = 2x$; $z = 3(x + y)$; $7\frac{1}{2}$, 15, $67\frac{1}{2}$

4. $x = 3y + 6$, $z = 2(x + y) - 2$, $x + y + z = 112$; 30, 8, 74

5. $2p + 10 = C$
   Subtract eq 1 from 2
   $2p = 16$, $p = 8$ people
   $4p - 6 = C$; $C$ (cost) = 26 pesos

## The Chinese Matrix Solution

### MATERIALS

Reproducible 30

### PROCEDURE

1. Distribute the handout.

2. Have students proceed as directed.

### ANSWERS

1. $x = -1, y = 1$

2. $p = \frac{1}{2}, g = 3$

3. $x = -4, y = -2$

4. $g + p = 100$        $g$ = good

   $300g + \frac{500}{7} p = 10,000$    $p$ = poor

   $12\frac{1}{2}$ good, $87\frac{1}{2}$ poor

5. $9g = 11s$             $g$ = gold
   $8g + s = 10s + g - 13$     $s$ = silver
   A silver piece weighs $29\frac{1}{4}$ oz. A gold piece weighs $35\frac{3}{4}$ oz.

## Systems of Three Linear Equations:   The Chinese Solution

### MATERIALS

Reproducible 31

### PROCEDURE

1. Distribute the handout.

2. Have students proceed as directed.

### ANSWERS

$x = 3, y = 2, z = -5$

# Systems of Equations
# from Guatemala

Spain was ruled by African Moors from 711 to 1492. During that time, it was the major entry to Europe for the advanced mathematics and science of the Islamic civilization. Mathematics books written in Arabic were translated in Spain and made available to European mathematicians. Some spelling changed. For example, the Arabic word *al-jabr* is now spelled "algebra."

Spain: A leader in mathematics in
the Middle Ages

It is not surprising that the first algebra book produced in the Americas was written in Spanish. Published in Mexico in 1556, it provided merchants with the basic algebra needed for practical problems. A more complete algebra book was published in Guatemala City in 1732. Titled *Noticia Breve de Todas las Reglas Mas Principales de la Arithmetica Practica*, it was written by Juan Joseph de Padilla. The following interesting puzzles by de Padilla can be solved as systems of equations:

1. In a battle for control of Spain, African Moors outnumbered Castilians 6 to 1. Castilians got 400 reenforcements and Moors got 600. This lowered the ratio of Moors to Castilians to 4 to 1. How many did each side have before and after reinforcement?

   _____

2. Two pieces of cloth were sold, the first at 2 *reales* per *vara* and the other at 4 *reales* per *vara*. The more expensive cloth was 30 *varas* longer than the shorter cloth. Its price was 3 times that of the shorter cloth. How long was each piece? (A *vara* was about .83 m.)

   _____

3. Together, the ages of Pedro, Juan, and Diego add up to 90 years. Juan is twice as old as Pedro, and Diego's age is 3 times the other two ages combined. How old is each?

   _____

4. Juan, Pedro, and Diego go in together to buy a cart that costs 112 pesos. Juan puts in 3 times Pedro's amount and 6 pesos more. Diego puts in 2 less than twice the amount put in by Pedro and Juan together. How much did each contribute?

   _____

5. Some people put in equal amounts of money to buy a co-worker a present. If each put in 2 pesos, they would be 10 pesos short of the purchase price. But if each put in 4 pesos, there would be a surplus of 6 pesos. How many people were there and how much did the present cost?

   _____

*Algebra Activities from Many Cultures*

Name _____

Date _____

# The Chinese Matrix Solution

The Chinese have always loved puzzles and patterns. Many of their puzzles involved the rice trade. To solve these puzzles, the Chinese invented the matrix method, an advanced method that we still use today. Calculations with rod numerals may have suggested this method. The following example is typical of problems the Chinese solved 2000 years ago:

> A farmer sells 2 measures of poor rice and 3 measures of good rice for 7 coins. He sells 4 measures of poor rice and 2 measures of good rice for only 6 coins. What is the cost of each type of rice?

In modern terms we would write this as a system of equations, using $p$ as the cost of a measure of **p**oor rice and $g$ as the cost of a measure of good rice:

$$2p + 3g = 7$$
$$4p + 2g = 6$$

## Step 1

To solve this kind of puzzle, the Chinese first set up a matrix, or grid, of numbers. They used only the coefficients and the constant terms. The coefficients and constant term of the first statement in the puzzle were put in one row, those of the second statement in a second row:

|       | poor | good | coins |
|-------|------|------|-------|
| Row 1 | 2    | 3    | 7     |
| Row 2 | 4    | 2    | 6     |

## Step 2

Find a multiplier that will make the first number in Row 1 the opposite of the first number in Row 2. In this case, the multiplier is –2 because $2 \times (-2) = -4$. Now multiply all the numbers in Row 1 by this multiplier.

| Row 1 | $2 \times (-2) = -4$ | $3 \times (-2) = -6$ | $7 \times (-2) = -14$ |
|-------|------|------|------|
| Row 2 | 4 | 2 | 6 |

## Step 3

Add the numbers in each column to get a new row:

| New row | 0 | –4 | –8 |
|---------|---|----|----|

The new row is equivalent to the equation: $-4g = -8$. Therefore, $g = 2$. Substitute $g = 2$ in the first equation to find $p$.

$$2p + 3g = 7$$
$$2p + 3(2) = 7$$
$$p = \tfrac{1}{2}$$

Good rice sold for 2 coins a measure, poor rice for $\tfrac{1}{2}$ coin.

*(continued)*

*Algebra Activities from Many Cultures*

Name _____

Date _____

# The Chinese Matrix Solution *(continued)*

Solve these systems of equations by using the Chinese method:

1. $3x + 5y = 2$

   $x + y = 0$

   $x =$ _____

   $y =$ _____

2. $2p + 3g = 10$

   $4p + 2g = 8$

   $x =$ _____

   $y =$ _____

3. $3x - 5y = -2$

   $4x - y = -14$

   $x =$ _____

   $y =$ _____

Solve these ancient Chinese examples using any method:

4. A Chinese family bought 100 units of land, some good and some poor, at a price of 10,000 gold coins. 1 unit of good land cost 300 gold coins. Poor land was priced at 7 units for 500 gold coins. How many units of each did they buy? Good land: _____ Poor land: _____

5. A group of 9 equal gold pieces weighs the same as a group of 11 equal silver pieces. One piece is taken from each group and put in the other. Now the gold lot weighs 13 ounces less than the silver. Find the weight of each piece. Gold: _____ Silver: _____

*Algebra Activities from Many Cultures*

# Systems of Three Linear Equations— The Chinese Solution

Two thousand years ago, Chinese mathematicians had invented a matrix method of solving systems of equations. That was 1500 years before matrices were used in Europe. We still employ the same Chinese method today, although graphing calculators can do some of the work for us. This example comes from ancient China. Given:

3 bundles top grade + 2 bundles medium grade + 1 bundle low grade make 39 *dou*.

2 bundles top grade + 3 bundles medium grade + 1 bundle low grade make 34 *dou*.

1 bundle top grade + 2 bundles medium grade + 3 bundles low grade make 26 *dou*.

What is the volume, in *dou*, of 1 bundle of each grade of rice?

Write 3 equations, letting $x$ = volume of 1 bundle of top grade, $y$ = volume of 1 bundle of medium grade, $z$ = volume of 1 bundle of low grade.

$$3x + 2y + z = 39$$
$$2x + 3y + z = 34$$
$$x + 2y + 3z = 26$$

Form a matrix using the coefficients and constants from the three statements.

| Row 1 | 3 | 2 | 1 | 39 |
|-------|---|---|---|----|
| Row 2 | 2 | 3 | 1 | 34 |
| Row 3 | 1 | 2 | 3 | 26 |

Each number in the first three columns stands for the coefficient of one of the variables. Converting the numbers in the first two columns to zero (0) will let you solve for the third variable. To do this, follow these steps:

Convert the numbers in the **first** column to zero (0).

## Step 1

First, multiply each number in Row 1 by the number in the **first** column of Row 2—in this case, 2. Call the result Row A. Next, multiply Row 2 by the number in the **first** column of Row 1— in this case, 3. Call the result Row B. Now subtract the number in each column of Row A from the number in each column of Row B. Call the result Row C.

| Row B | 6 | 9 | 3 | 102 |
|-------|---|---|----|-----|
| –Row A | – 6 | – 4 | –2 | – 78 |
| Row C | 0 | 5 | 1 | 24 |

*(continued)*

# Systems of Three Linear Equations—
# The Chinese Solution (continued)

## Step 2

In step 1, you worked with Rows 1 and 2. Here we use Rows 1 and 3. Multiply Row 3 by 3 to get Row D.

| Row 1 | 3 | 2 | 1 | 39 |
|---|---|---|---|---|
| Row 3 | 1 | 2 | 3 | 26 |
| Row D | 3 | 6 | 9 | 78 |

Now subtract Row 1 from Row D. Call the result Row E.

| Row D | 3 | 6 | 9 | 78 |
|---|---|---|---|---|
| –Row 1 | –3 | –2 | –1 | –39 |
| Row E | 0 | 4 | 8 | 39 |

Row E has a zero (0) in the first column for a simpler matrix.

## Step 3

Now that you have converted the numbers in the first column to zero (0), you need to convert the number in the **second** column to zero (0), too.

First, multiply Row E by the number in the **second** column of Row C—in this case, 5. Call the result Row F. Multiply Row C by the number in the **second** column of Row E—in this case, 4. Call the result Row G. Then subtract Row G from Row F. Call the result Row H.

| Row F | 0 | 20 | 40 | 195 |
|---|---|---|---|---|
| –Row G | –0 | –20 | –4 | –96 |
| Row H | 0 | 0 | 36 | 99 |

*(continued)*

*Algebra Activities from Many Cultures*

# Systems of Three Linear Equations—
## The Chinese Solution *(continued)*

### Step 4

The first two columns in the row now contain zero (0). You can now find the value of the third variable. Remember, the numbers in the first three columns are the coefficients of the variables, and the number in the fourth column is the constant. So we can read Row H as:

0 bundles top grade plus 0 bundles medium grade plus 36 bundles low grade make 99 *dou* ($0x + 0y + 36z = 99$; $36z = 99$)

or

1 bundle low grade makes $2\frac{3}{4}$ *dou* ($z = 2\frac{3}{4}$).

### Step 5

Substitute $z = 2\frac{3}{4}$ in equations 2 and 3:

$$2x + 3y = 31\frac{1}{4}$$

$$x + 2y = 17\frac{3}{4}$$

Again, set up a matrix using the coefficients and constants to solve for the second variable. Substituting this new value will allow you to solve for the third variable.

$$x = 9\frac{1}{4} \ dou, y = 4\frac{1}{4} \ dou, z = 2\frac{3}{4} \ dou$$

Use the Chinese matrix method to solve:

$$3x + 5y + z = 14$$
$$x + 3y + z = 4$$
$$x + 2y + 4z = -13$$

*Algebra Activities from Many Cultures*

# Proportion and Variation

## Multicultural Examples

### MATERIALS

Reproducible 32

### ANSWERS

1. $\frac{50}{24} = \frac{\left(4\frac{1}{2}\right)}{x}$; $x = 2.16$ measures of rice

2. $\frac{\left(\frac{3}{7}\right)}{\left(2\frac{1}{2}\right)} = \frac{9}{x}$; $x = \frac{9\left(\frac{5}{2}\right)}{\frac{3}{4}}$, or 52.5 palas of saffron

### EXTENSION ACTIVITY

Community group research project

Bring in examples of proportional thinking used in your community. Discuss these examples in your group and prepare a group presentation for the class.

## Aztec Land Taxes

### MATERIALS

Reproducible 33

### ANSWERS

1. Graph

2. (a) Straight line, directly

   (b) $T_c = 0.1q$, $T$ in cacao beans, $q$ the number of *quahuitls* of farm area. The cacao bean tax is rounded to the nearest unit.

   (c) $T_b = 5$, $T_b$ = taxes on bundles of firewood;
   $T_t = 2$, $T_t$ = taxes on turkeys

   (d) Answers will vary.

## Money Changers in Colonial Mexico

### MATERIALS

Reproducible 34

### ANSWERS

1. Let $x$ = price of a small jug.
   $\frac{125}{100} = \frac{1}{x}$; $x = \frac{100}{125} = 0.8$ peso per small jug; total price, 1800 pesos

2. $\frac{9}{7} = \frac{72}{x}$; $x = 56$ pesos

3. $\frac{15}{14} = \frac{x}{42}$; $x = 45$ crowns

4. $\frac{14}{15} = \frac{x}{60}$; $x = 56$ ducats

# Multicultural Examples

Proportional thinking was central to science and mathematics when the pharaohs ruled Egypt. A higher Nile River flood meant more farm land could be watered. A lower Nile River flood watered less land. Taxes were directly proportional to the size of the crop. Buildings constructed from a plan were enlarged proportionally. Equations were solved with proportional thinking. Proportional relations are also called "direct variation."

**Egyptian Example:** Suppose you had a crop of 450 *hekats* of barley. The pharaoh's tax is 1 *hekat* out of every 10 *hekats*. To find the tax, *t*, you could set up a proportion:

$$\frac{10}{1} = \frac{450}{t}$$
$$t = \frac{450}{10}, \text{ or } 45 \text{ hekats.}$$

Proportions were also part of the mathematics of Mesopotamia, India, and China. In the Middle Ages, Arabic-speaking mathematicians introduced proportional methods into Europe, where they were called "the rule of three." The rule of three showed how to get the fourth term of a proportion if you knew the other three. In general terms, given $\frac{a}{b} = \frac{c}{x}$, then:

$$x = \frac{bc}{a}.$$

**Directions:** Use a proportion, or "rule of three," in these examples.

1. The Chinese book *Jiuzhang,* dating back to 1000 B.C.E., asks:

   How much rice is exchanged for $4\frac{1}{2}$ measures of millet if 50 measures of millet are exchanged for 24 measures of rice?

**Tax collectors**

_____

2. Bhaskara, an Indian mathematician, c. 600 C.E., asked:

   If $2\frac{1}{2}$ palas of saffron are purchased for $\frac{3}{7}$ of a niska, how many palas can be bought for 9 niskas?

_____

3. Write a skit for a tax collection scene in ancient Egypt. The farmer cannot hide his growing crop but still tries to argue with the tax collector.

_____

*Algebra Activities from Many Cultures*

Name _____

Date _____

# Aztec Land Taxes

"Everything is sold by count and measure . . ." observed Hernán Cortes, the Spanish army officer, when he first saw the market at the Aztec capital of Tenochtitlán. Still, little about Aztec mathematics is known today. Spanish conquerors destroyed the Aztec records. Only a few documents escaped. Recent study of a 1545 Aztec tax record has revealed some unsuspected features of Aztec mathematics. The numerals on the tax record had positional value, and used a corn symbol as a zero placeholder. Aztec  measurements of  area were more accurate than Spanish measurements of the same farms. Here are some figures based on these records showing different types of taxes. Some taxes were fixed but other taxes varied from farm to farm.

| Taxes and Areas of Aztec Farms at Tepetlaoztoc, 1545 (Area in Square *Quahuitls*, about 2.5 m $\times$ 2.5 m) | | | |
|---|---|---|---|
| Area | Cacao Beans | Firewood | Turkeys |
| 97 | 10 | 5 bundles | 2 |
| 140 | 14 | 5 bundles | 2 |
| 160 | 16 | 5 bundles | 2 |
| 180 | 18 | 5 bundles | 2 |
| 250 | 25 | 5 bundles | 2 |
| 300 | 30 | 5 bundles | 2 |
| 346 | 35 | 5 bundles | 2 |
| 551 | 55 | 5 bundles | 2 |

## Questions for Critical Thinking

1. Using area as the first coordinate, and the number of cacao beans for the second coordinate, plot points for values given in the table. Connect the points with as smooth a line as possible.

2. Group discussion:

   (a) Is the graph a straight line or a curve? Does the tax in cacao beans vary directly, or indirectly with the area of the farm? _____

   (b) Write an equation that relates the tax in cacao beans to the area of the farms. _____

   (c) What is the equation for the taxes that do not vary? _____

   (d) Do you think the cacao bean tax was a fair tax? Do you think the fixed tax of firewood and turkeys were fair taxes? _____

*Algebra Activities from Many Cultures*

Name _____

Date _____

# Money Changers in Colonial Mexico

The first American mathematics book in a European language was *Sumario Compendioso*, by Juan Diez. It was published in Spanish in Mexico City, in 1556. Much of the *Sumario Compendioso* is concerned with the use of proportions to calculate exchange rates.

Many different kind of coins were used in colonial Mexico City. Figuring out the exchange rates required experts. Ducats exchanged at 6 ducats to 5 pesos. The ratio of crowns to pesos was 9 to 7. However, ducats to crowns were 14 to 15. Then as now, international exchange was figured from prepared tables. Some examples of exchange rates in colonial Mexico City are listed below. Notice the influence of Arabic culture on the Spanish language. The word "tomin" comes from the Arabic word for eight. "Maravedis" were a coin from the Moorish dynasty of Murabitin.

$$12 \; granos \; = \; 1 \; tomin$$

$$1 \; tomin \; = \; \tfrac{1}{8} \; peso$$

$$\tfrac{1}{8} \; peso \; = \; \tfrac{1}{3} \; drachm$$

$$1 \; tomin \; = \; 56 \; maravedis$$

Use proportions to answer these questions from *Sumario Compendioso* by Juan Diez:

1. I have 2000 jugs; 1000 jugs are 25% larger than the other 1000 jugs. I will sell them at a price proportional to size. If the large jugs sell for 1 peso, what should I get for all the jugs?

   _____

2. If 9 crowns exchanged for 7 pesos, how many pesos were exchanged for 72 crowns?

   _____

3. If crowns and ducats exchanged in the ratio of 15 to 14, how many crowns exchanged for 42 ducats?

   _____

4. If ducats and crowns exchanged in the ratio of 14 to 15, how many ducats exchanged for 60 crowns?

   _____

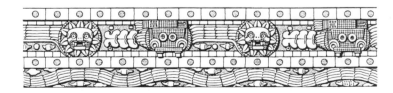

*Algebra Activities from Many Cultures*

# Quadratic Equations

## The Multicultural Origin of the Quadratic Formula

### MATERIALS

Reproducible 35
construction paper or other heavy paper
scissors

### PROCEDURE

1. Distribute the handout.

2. Introduce students to the early mathematicians.

3. Guide students through the use of paper cutouts to create geometric models for quadratic equations. Have them follow the step-by-step procedure outlined on the handout.

### ANSWERS

1. $x = 3$

2. Answers will vary.

3. 3

4. Answers will vary.

5. $x = 4$

6. $x = 3$

## Quadratic Equations from Mexico and Guatemala

### MATERIALS

Reproducible 36

### ANSWERS

1. Diez gave these pairs: (3,4) and ($1^{12}/_{13}$ and $4^{8}/_{13}$). Any two lengths for legs of a right triangle would work because $a^2 + b^2 = c^2$.

2. $^{81}/_4$

   $x^2 - 15^3/_4 = x$

3. 35 pesos.
   $x^2 + x = 1260$

4. 150. $4x^2 = 90,000$

5. 20 leagues

6. 8 mares, 40 cows

7. 6 sons and 9 daughters. Let number of sons = $2x$, daughters $3x$; $6x^2 (2x/2) = 162$, $x = 3$

8. 8, 12

9. 15, 17

10. 6, 12, 24, $x$, $2x$, $4x$; $2x^2 = 12x$

11. 7, 13

12. 10, 30, $3x^2 + 12x = 420$

## Quadratic Equations with Fractions

### MATERIALS

Reproducible 37

### ANSWERS

4, 8

# The Multicultural Origin
# of the Quadratic Formula

The ancient mathematics of Mesopotamia and Egypt never died. We are continuing the ancient mathematics every time we use the quadratic formula. Ancient Babylonians used a form of the quadratic formula to solve equations 4000 years ago. The quadratic formula was introduced to Europe in the Middle Ages through algebra books written by al-Khwarizmi, Abu Kamil, and others. They wrote in Arabic, the language of science of that time, but neither mathematician was Arabic. Abu Kamil was Egyptian. Al-Khwarizmi was from a Central Asian region then known as Khwarizm. Uzbek and Turkomen languages are spoken in the area of Khwarizm.

## AL-KHWARIZMI'S GEOMETRIC MODELS

A feature of the first algebra books was the use of geometric models. You can cut out heavy paper rectangles or use algebra tiles to make these models.

### Model $x^2 + 16x = 36$

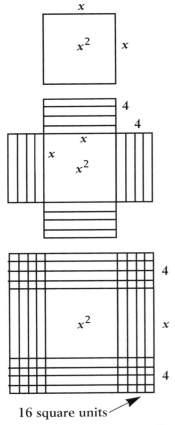

**Step 1.** Make a square with sides $x$. The area of this square is $x^2$.

**Step 2.** Take 16 strips, each $x$ units long and 1 unit wide, to model $16x$. Divide evenly in 4 groups. Place 4 strips on each side of the square, $x^2$. You now have an area of $x^2 + 16x$. This area equals 36 square units because $x^2 + 16x = 36$.

**Step 3.** Fill the 4 corners to make an enlarged square. It will take 16 unit-squares in each corner, a total of 64. You have added 64 to the 36 square units. The total area of the enlarged square is 100 square units. The side of the enlarged square is 10 units long.

16 square units

*(continued)*

*Algebra Activities from Many Cultures*

# The Multicultural Origin of the Quadratic Formula *(continued)*

**Step 4.** Find the value of $x$, the side of the original square. The side of the large square is 10 units long. The lengths of the segments of the side are 4, $x$, and 4. So $x + 8 = 10$, and $x = 2$.

Check.

$x^2 + 16x = 36$

$2^2 + 16(2) = 36$

$36 = 36$.

## MORE GEOMETRIC MODELS FROM AL-KHWARIZMI

### Model $x^2 + 10x = 39$

You will need one square of $x$ by $x$, and 10 rectangles, each $x$ by 1. You can cut out rectangles from heavy paper. To use rectangles that are $x$ by $^1/_2$, cut the $x$ by 1 rectangle in half, lengthwise.

**Step 1.** Model $x^2$ with a square of side $x$. Model $10x$ with 10 rectangles each 1 by $x$.

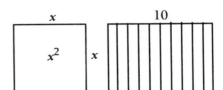

**Step 2.** Divide $10x$ by 4. Get $2\frac{1}{2} x$. Add $2\frac{1}{2}$ of the $x$ by 1 strips on each side of the square. The area now equals 39.

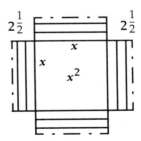

**Step 3.** Complete the square. Fill each corner with $(2\frac{1}{2})^2 = \frac{25}{4}$ unit squares. The area now equals $39 + 25 = 64$.

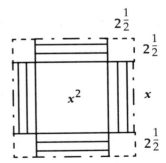

**Step 4.** The large square of area 64 has sides of 8 units. Subtract the lengths of the corners. $x = 8 - 2(\frac{5}{2}) = 3$; the solution is $x = 3$.

*(continued)*

© 1997 Beatrice Lumpkin
J. Weston Walch, Publisher

73

*Algebra Activities from Many Cultures*

# The Multicultural Origin of the Quadratic Formula *(continued)*

1. Solve $x^2 + 10x = 39$ algebraically, by completing the square.

   $x =$ _____

2. How does the algebraic method of completing the square compare with al-Khwarizmi's geometric method of completing the square?

   _____

   _____

   _____

3. Solve $x^2 + 10x = 39$ with the use of the quadratic formula:

   For $ax^2 + bx + c = 0$, $x = \dfrac{-b \pm \sqrt{b^2 - 4ac}}{2a}$

   $x =$ _____

4. Compare your solution or solutions with the above solution(s) from al-Khwarizmi's geometric method. How are they the same? How are they different?

   _____

   _____

   _____

5. Use the method of al-Khwarizmi to make geometric models to solve:

   $x^2 + 8x = 48$, $x^2 + 12x = 45$

   $x =$ _____

6. Try an alternative method of completing the square for equation $x^2 + 10x = 39$. Place five of the $x$-by-1 strips on two adjacent sides of the $x$-square. Then use unit squares to fill in the corner. Complete the solution.

   $x =$ _____

# Quadratic Equations from Mexico and Guatemala

Examples 1–7 were written by Juan Diez in Mexico City in 1556. Examples 8–12 are adapted from a book by Juan Joseph de Padilla, printed in Guatemala, 1732. You can solve these puzzles with quadratic equations and other strategies.

1. Find two numbers whose squares added together give a perfect square.

2. Find a perfect square with this property: If $15\frac{3}{4}$ is subtracted from this perfect square, the remainder is the root of the square.

3. A traveler wants passage on a ship and asks the captain what he charges. The captain says that it will not be more than other passengers pay. "How much?" asked the traveler, again. "It will be the number of pesos which squared, and added to the number, gives 1260," the captain replied. What was the fare?

4. A merchant inquired how many goats were for sale. The owner of the goats enjoyed puzzles. So he replied, "If the number of goats were squared, and the square quadrupled, the result will be 90,000." How many goats?

5. A traveler asked how many leagues it was to a certain place. The reply was, "Square the number and divide the result by 5. Then the quotient is 80." How far was it?

6. How many mares and cows does a farmer have if there are five times as many cows as mares, and the sum of the squares of the number of each is 1664?

7. A couple has sons and daughters in the ratio of 2 to 3. If you multiply the numbers of sons by the number of daughters, then multiply the product by half the number of sons, the final product will be 162. How many of each?

8. Find two numbers whose sum is 20 and the difference of their squares is 80.

9. Find two numbers whose difference is 2 and the difference of their squares is 64.

10. Find three numbers in the ratio of 1:2:4 if the product of the first two is triple the third number.

11. Find two numbers whose sum is 20 and whose product is 91.

12. Find three numbers, given that the second is triple the first and the third number is 4. Multiply the first by the second and the second by the third. The sum of these products is 420.

*Algebra Activities from Many Cultures*

# Quadratic Equations with Fractions

About the year 880 in Cairo, Egypt, Abu Kamil showed how to work with equations for fractions. For example, he solved this puzzle:

Find two numbers whose sum is 10. If you divide 10 by one of these numbers, then multiply by 10 divided by the other unknown number, the result is $6\frac{1}{4}$.

Let the unknown numbers be $x$ and $10 - x$.

$$\frac{10}{x} \cdot \frac{10}{10-x} = 6\frac{1}{4}$$

Multiply the fractions $\dfrac{100}{x(10-x)} = 6\frac{1}{4}$

Multiply both sides of the equation by $x(10-x)$ and simplify.
$$100 = 62.5x - 6.25x^2$$

Divide both sides by 6.25 and rearrange terms.
$$x^2 - 10x + 16 = 0$$
$$x = 8, 2$$

Checking the solutions in the original problem,

$$(\tfrac{10}{8})(\tfrac{10}{2}) = \tfrac{100}{16} = 6\tfrac{1}{4}$$

$$(\tfrac{10}{2})(\tfrac{10}{8}) = \tfrac{100}{16} = 6\tfrac{1}{4}$$

**Solve this puzzle:**

Find two numbers whose sum is 12. If you divide 12 by one of these numbers, then multiply by 12 divided by the other unknown number, the result is $4\frac{1}{2}$.

Hint: Let $x$ = one number. Let $12 - x$ = the other number.

*Algebra Activities from Many Cultures*

# Radicals and Exponents

## Compound Interest in Babylonia

### Materials

Reproducible 38

### ANSWERS

1. 5.38 shekels

2.

| Year | Amount, beginning of year | Interest | Amount, end of year |
|------|---------------------------|----------|---------------------|
| Year 1 | 1000 | 200 | 1200 |
| Year 2 | 1200 | 240 | 1440 |
| Year 3 | 1440 | 288 | 1728 |
| Year 4 | 1728 | 345.60 | 2073.60 |
| Year 5 | 2073.60 | 414.72 | 2488.32 |
| Year 6 | 2488.32 | 497.66 | 2985.98 |
| Year 7 | 2985.98 | 597.20 | 3583.18 |

3. $(3000 - 2985.98)/(3583.18 - 2985.98) = 0.0235$

check $1000(1.2)^{6.0235} = 2998.81$,
error $1.19
Principal tripled in 6.023 years.
Graph is a curve.

## Logarithms in Babylonia

### MATERIALS

Reproducible 39
graph paper
scissors

### ANSWERS

1. Values increase .25, powers of 2

2. 1.75      128
   2         256

3.

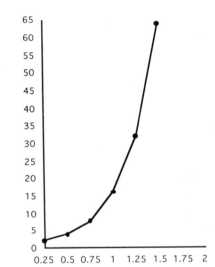

4.

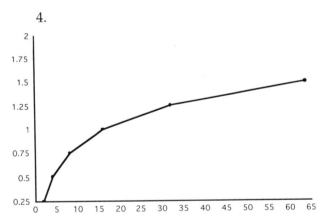

5. They are inverses, reflected across the line $y = x$.

6. 16

## Laws of Exponents from Iraq

### MATERIALS

Reproducible 40

### ANSWERS

1.–3. Answers will vary.

4. $10x^3 + x^2 + 4x + 10 + 8x^{-2} + 2x^{-3}$

## Square Roots in Ancient Egypt

### MATERIALS

Reproducible 41

### ANSWER

2. 16 cubits, 12 cubits

## Square Roots in India

### MATERIALS

Reproducible 42

### ANSWERS

1. 1.414215686, 0.000002 or $2 \times 10^{-6}$

2. (a) 1.414213502 − 1.414213562 = 0.00000006 or $6 \times 10^{-7}$
   (b) 0.0000014 or $1.4 \times 10^{-6}$

# Compound Interest in Babylonia: Fractional Exponents

Problems of interest on loans are not new. A large part of a country's payments on the national debt is used to pay interest on the debt. This does not reduce the principal, or the original amount of the debt. People in Babylonia 4000 years ago also paid interest on their loans. Their bankers asked questions such as, "How many years would it take to double your money if you invested it at 20% interest, compounded annually?"

Today a banker would find the answer in a table in her computer. The Babylonians also made up a table. Their table listed annual interest as shown below. Suppose the investor began with an amount, or principal, of 1000 shekels:

| Principal | 1000.00 shekels |
|---|---|
| End of year 1 | 1200.00 shekels |
| End of year 2 | 1440.00 shekels |
| End of year 3 | 1728.00 shekels |
| End of year 4 | 2073.60 shekels |

**Cuneiform tablet**

The Babylonian bankers paid the interest that was due to the day, even if the money was withdrawn before the end of the year. Their table showed that money loaned at 20% interest would double at a fraction of a year more than 3 years. To find the needed fraction of a year, they "interpolated" between the 3 year amount and the 4 year amount.

| End of year 3 | 1728.00 shekels |
|---|---|
| 3 years + ?? | 2000.00 shekels |
| End of year 4 | 2073.60 shekels |

$$\frac{2000.00 - 1728.00}{2073.60 - 1728.00} = 0.7870 \text{ year}$$

The Babylonians added 0.7870 year to 3 years and said the principal would double in 3.787 years.

## Questions for Critical Thinking

1. Was the Babylonian answer correct? Would the principal double in 3.787 years at 20% interest compounded annually? Check the Babylonian result with your calculator, using the formula $A = p(1 + r)^t$. Does $1000(1 + .20)^{3.787} = 2000$? If not, how large was the error? _____

*(continued)*

# Compound Interest in Babylonia: Fractional Exponents
## (continued)

2. Make a table to find out how long it would take to triple 1000 shekels of silver invested at 20% interest, compounded annually.

| Year | Savings at beginning of year | Interest | Savings at end of year |
|------|------------------------------|----------|------------------------|
| Year 1 | 1000 shekels | | |
| Year 2 | | | |
| Year 3 | | | |
| Year 4 | | | |
| Year 5 | | | |
| Year 6 | | | |
| Year 7 | | | |

## Project

3. The Babylonians used proportions to interpolate between years in their table. This method is accurate only if the graph of the equation is a straight line, in other words, only if the equation is linear. However, for a short distance on a curve, the error may be small.

Plot the values in your table on graph paper. Use time in years as the x-axis, and the amount on the y-axis. Connect the points with as smooth a line as possible. Do you get a straight line? a curve?

# Logarithms in Babylonia

Modern algebra can be used to find the number of years required to triple $1000 invested at 20% interest. From the formula $A = p(1 + r)^t$, we get the equation $3 = 1.2^x$.

$3 = 1.2^x$.

$\log 3 = x \log 1.2$

$\dfrac{\log 3}{\log 1.2} = x$

$x = 6.0257$ years

Were the Babylonian scribes experimenting with logarithms back in 1800 B.C.E? A clay tablet found in Iraq showed the following table:

| | |
|------|----|
| 0.25 | 2 |
| 0.5 | 4 |
| 0.75 | 8 |
| 1 | 16 |
| 1.25 | 32 |
| 1.5 | 64 |

## GROUP PROJECT

1. There was no text explaining this tablet. Do you see any number patterns in this table?

   _____

2. Predict the next two rows for this table. _____

3. Plot the pairs of values on graph paper, letting the first column be the first coordinate. Connect the points.

4. Plot the pairs of values on graph paper, letting the second column be the first coordinate. Connect the points as smoothly as possible.

5. Compare the two graphs you made for questions 3 and 4. Do you see a relation between them? Can you find graphs like that in your advanced algebra textbook? Hint: Look for exponential and logarithmic curves. _____

   _____

6. Mathematicians believe that the first column of the Babylonian table lists logarithms for the numbers in the second column. Remember that logarithms are exponents. What base were the Babylonians using? _____

*Algebra Activities from Many Cultures*

# The Laws of Exponents from Iraq

In the year 830, the first *al-jabr* (or algebra) book reached Europe. Algebra has become much easier since then. The use of exponents has made equations easier to write and to solve. In the first *al-jabr* book, the unknown was called the side of a square. Square and cube numbers were pictured as actual squares and cubes. But how could a fourth degree be illustrated? Or an eighth degree?

In Egypt, c 1000, Ibn al-Haytham was creating new mathematics to describe his experiments with light. Mathematicians of that time wrote "square-square" where we would write $x^4$. For $x^8$ they used to write "square-square-square-square." That seems clumsy to us but it showed that they used the laws of exponents: $x^8 = x^2\, x^2\, x^2\, x^2$. About 1180, a 19-year-old mathematician named al-Samaw'al put it all together in his book *The Shining*. He knew that he had something really important. Al Samaw'al is one of several scholars of Jewish background who made important contributions to Islamic mathematics.

Here are some examples used by al-Samaw'al, shown here with modern exponents.

$$2^2\, 2^2 = 2^4 \qquad\qquad (\tfrac{1}{2})^2(\tfrac{1}{2})^2 = (\tfrac{1}{2})^4$$

$$2^2\, 2^3 = 2^5 \qquad\qquad (\tfrac{1}{2})^3(\tfrac{1}{2})^3(\tfrac{1}{2})^3 = (\tfrac{1}{2})^9$$

$$2^2\, 2^2\, 2^3 = 2^7 \qquad\qquad (\tfrac{1}{2})^2(\tfrac{1}{2})^3(\tfrac{1}{2})^3 = (\tfrac{1}{2})^8$$

$$x^{-3}x^{-4} = x^{-7}$$

$$x^n x^{-m} = x^{(n-m)}$$

Al-Samaw'al also figured out the modern method of division of polynomials. He showed how to do the division shown below. (For convenience, the examples are shown with modern exponents.)

$$\frac{20x^6 + 2x^5 + 58x^4 + 75x^3 + 125x^2 + 96x + 94 + 140x^{-1} + 50x^{-2} + 90x^{-3} + 20x^{-4}}{2x^3 + 5x + 5 + 10x^{-1}}$$

Al-Samaw'al wrote only the coefficients and kept the powers in columns. Today we do the same thing in synthetic division. He also knew and made good use of the rules for operations on signed numbers. The little known name of al-Samawa'al belongs on the honor roll of those who made algebra easier for us today.

*(continued)*

*Algebra Activities from Many Cultures*

Name _____

Date _____

# The Laws of Exponents from Iraq *(continued)*

## Questions for Critical Thinking

1. Al-Samaw'al made his living as a physician, yet he was on the cutting edge of new mathematics. Do you think that would be possible today? Why or why not?

   _____

   _____

   _____

2. Al-Samaw'al taught himself advanced mathematics and became a great mathematician. Do you think that would be possible today? Explain.

   _____

   _____

   _____

3. Rules for operations on exponents and on signed numbers were part of al-Samaw'al's work. For example, he knew that $\dfrac{a^{-3}}{a^{-5}} = a^2$, $a \neq 0$.

   In your own words, explain:
   (a) The laws of exponents used in this example.

   _____

   _____

   (b) The rule for signs used in this example.

   _____

   _____

## Project

Complete the division example from al-Samaw'al:

$$\frac{20x^6 + 2x^5 + 58x^4 + 75x^3 + 125x^2 + 96x + 94 + 140x^{-1} + 50x^{-2} + 90x^{-3} + 20x^{-4}}{2x^3 + 5x + 5 + 10x^{-1}}$$

Name _____

Date _____

# Square Roots in Ancient Egypt

Only a small percent of ancient Egyptian papyri have survived. These are scattered in museums and private collections around the world. A mathematical papyrus in a Berlin museum asks questions that involve finding the square roots of fractions.

## Example 1

Find the sides of two squares whose sum is 100 cubits$^2$, given that the smaller has a side $\frac{3}{4}$ the length of the side of the larger square.

$$\boxed{\phantom{xxx}} \quad + \quad \boxed{\phantom{xx}} \quad = \quad \boxed{\begin{array}{c}100 \text{ square} \\ \text{cubits}\end{array}}$$

The method of solution was 1) to choose any convenient value, and 2) try it to see how big an error resulted. Finally, they made the necessary proportional correction. This method was called "false position."

1. The scribe chose an assumed value of 1 cubit for the larger side. Then the smaller square would have a side of $\frac{3}{4}$ cubit.

2. Add the areas.  $(1)^2 + (\frac{3}{4})^2 = 1\frac{9}{16}$, or $\frac{25}{16}$.

   The combined areas make a square of area $\frac{25}{16}$ cubit$^2$. **To find the side of this square, take the square root of $\frac{25}{16}$ cubit$^2$. It is $\frac{5}{4}$ cubits.** But the side of a square of 100 cubits$^2$ is 10 cubits, not $\frac{5}{4}$ cubits.

3. To correct $\frac{5}{4}$ to get 10, multiply by $10/(\frac{5}{4})$ or 8. Multiply the assumed value of 1 cubit to get a side of 8 cubits. The other side is $(\frac{3}{4})8 = 6$ cubits.

4. Proof: (8 cubits)$^2$ + (6 cubits)$^2$ = 100 cubits$^2$.

**Work with a Partner:** You can solve a similar problem from the Berlin Papyrus by using an assumed value (false position). To find the correction factor, first be sure to take the square root of the desired sum. You will also need the square root of the sum of the two squares that result from your assumed value.

## BERLIN PAPYRUS

### Example 2

Find the sides of two squares whose sum is 400 cubits$^2$, given that the ratio of the side of the smaller to the side of the larger square is $1\frac{1}{2}$ to 2.

Hint:  Assume that the sides are 2 cubits and $1\frac{1}{2}$ cubits.

*Algebra Activities from Many Cultures*

# Square Roots in India

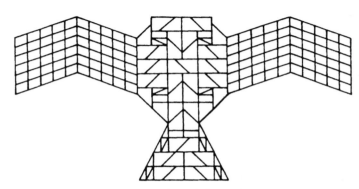

**A Prastara Altar (after Thibaut)**

The Indian *sutras* were very brief verses used for instruction in India as early as 800 B.C.E. Much of what we know of ancient Indian mathematics comes from verses called *sulba-sutras*. These verses gave formulas for measurement and construction of altars on which offerings would be placed. The accuracy of the altar design was extremely important in the Indian religion of that time. One way to check the accuracy of right angles in a square base is to carefully measure the diagonal of the square. The builders would have to know a good approximation for the value of $\sqrt{2}$.

A sulba-sutra from about 700 B.C.E. gave the following formula:

$$\sqrt{2} = 1 + \frac{1}{3} + \frac{1}{(3 \times 4)} - \frac{1}{(3 \times 4 \times 34)}$$

## CALCULATOR EXPLORATION

1. Use the above formula to find the ancient Indian value for $\sqrt{2}$. What is the difference between the ancient and modern values, to the nearest millionths?

   _____

2. Two thousand years after the value for $\sqrt{2}$ was given as
   $\sqrt{2} = 1 + \frac{1}{3} + \frac{1}{(3 \times 4)} - \frac{1}{(3 \times 4 \times 34)}$ another Indian mathematician improved the ancient value by adding two terms. The new value was:
   $\sqrt{2} = 1 + \frac{1}{3} + \frac{1}{(3 \times 4)} - \frac{1}{(3 \times 4 \times 34)} - \frac{1}{(3 \times 4 \times 34 \times 33)} + \frac{1}{(3 \times 4 \times 34 \times 34)}$.

   (a) What is the difference between the revised ancient value for $\sqrt{2}$ and the modern value?

   _____

   (b) How much accuracy was gained by revising the ancient value?

   _____

*Algebra Activities from Many Cultures*

# Higher Degree Equations

## Using Tables to Solve Cubic Equations in Babylonia

### MATERIALS

Reproducible 43

### PROCEDURE

1. Distribute the handout.

2. Have students create a table of squares and cubes of integers 5 through 20 to help them solve the problems in this unit.

### ANSWERS

| Number | Square | Cube | Sum of Square and Cube |
|--------|--------|------|------------------------|
| 5 | 25 | 125 | 150 |
| 6 | 36 | 216 | 252 |
| 7 | 49 | 343 | 392 |
| 8 | 64 | 512 | 576 |
| 9 | 81 | 729 | 810 |
| 10 | 100 | 1000 | 1100 |
| 11 | 121 | 1331 | 1452 |
| 12 | 144 | 1728 | 1872 |
| 13 | 169 | 2197 | 2366 |
| 14 | 196 | 2744 | 2940 |
| 15 | 225 | 3375 | 3600 |
| 16 | 256 | 4096 | 4352 |
| 17 | 289 | 4913 | 5202 |
| 18 | 324 | 5832 | 6156 |
| 19 | 361 | 6859 | 7220 |
| 20 | 400 | 8000 | 8400 |

1. $3x^3 + 2x^2 = 1664$, $x = 8$.
   Multiply equation by $a^2/b^3$, $a = 3$, $b = 2$.
   $(9/8)3x^3 + (9/8)2x^2 = (9/8)1664$
   $(27/8)x^3 + (9/4)x^2 = 1872$
   Substitute $y = (3/2)x$. Then $y^3 = (27/8)x^3$, $y^2 = (9/4)x^2$
   $y^3 + y^2 = 1872$
   From the Babylonian table of squares and cubes of integers, we find that $y = 12$.
   Since $y = (3/2)x$, $x = 8$.

2. $144x^3 + 12x^2 = 21$
   This is already in the form of $a^2 x^3 + a x^2 = c$.
   We can easily put it in the form of $a^3 x^3 + a^2 x^2 = ac$.
   Just multiply both sides by $a = 12$. Then, $(12)^3 x^3 + (12)^2 x^2 = 21(12)$.
   Substitute $y = 12x$.
   $y^3 + y^2 = 252$.
   From the Babylonian table of the sums of squares and cubes of integers, we find that $y = 6$. Since $y = 12x$, $x = \frac{1}{2}$ or 0.5.

## Cubic Equations from Umar al-Khayyami (Omar Khayyam)

### MATERIALS

Reproducible 44
graphing calculator

### ANSWERS

3. $x = 3, -1, -2$; yes

86

# Using Tables to Solve
# Cubic Equations in Babylonia

Babylonian scribes used tables to solve some third-degree equations. These tables showed integers, their squares, their cubes, and the sum of the square plus the cube. Equations can be solved with these tables if they can be transformed into the form $y^3 + y^2 = c$, where $c$ is a constant.

Complete the following table of squares and cubes of integers 5 to 20. For an interesting science fair project, the table could be written in cuneiform numerals and pressed into a clay tablet.

| Number | Square | Cube | Sum of Square and Cube |
|:---:|:---:|:---:|:---:|
| 5 | 25 | 125 | 150 |
| 6 | | | |
| 7 | | | |
| 8 | | | |
| 9 | | | |
| 10 | | | |
| 11 | | | |
| 12 | | | |
| 13 | | | |
| 14 | | | |
| 15 | | | |
| 16 | | | |
| 17 | | | |
| 18 | | | |
| 19 | | | |
| 20 | | | |

*(continued)*

# Using Tables to Solve Cubic Equations in Babylonia *(continued)*

**Example:**  $4x^3 + 2x^2 = 3078.$   *Multiply through by 2.*

$8x^3 + 4x^2 = 6156.$   *We can think of this as:*

$(2x)^3 + (2x)^2 = 6156.$   *Substitute y = 2x.*

$y^3 + y^2 = 6156$

From the row for 18 in our table for the Sums of Squares and Cubes, we have:

$$5832 + 324 = 6156.$$

Therefore $y = 18$. Since $y = 2x$, if $y = 18$, then $x = 9$.

In the general case of $ax^3 + bx^2 = c$, to change to the form, $y^3 + y^2 = c$, multiply both sides by $a^2/b^3$. Then substitute $y = ax/b$.

## PROJECT

Solve with the aid of the table of cubes and squares.

1. $3x^3 + 2x^2 = 1664.$

2. $144x^3 + 12x^2 = 21.$

*Algebra Activities from Many Cultures*

# Cubic Equations from
# Umar al-Khayyami (Omar Khayyam)

Umar al-Khayyami is remembered in the West as a romantic poet, author of the *Rubaiyat*. In his native Central Asia of Iran and Uzbekistan, al-Khayyami was better known as a scientist and mathematician; his poetry was only a sideline. Like most mathematicians of his time, 1050–1122, he was also an astronomer and philosopher. To survive, he became a politician, serving as vizier, or prime minister, to Malik Shah.

One of al-Khayyami's duties was to serve as the Shah's personal astrologer. But his real interest was scientific astronomy. He produced a more accurate calendar than the one we use today. It was accurate to 1 day in 5000 years. By the time he was 25, he had already written his famous *Algebra*. Al-Khayyami's *Algebra* makes a systematic study of cubic equations.

## EXAMPLES OF AL-KHAYYAMI'S CUBIC EQUATIONS

Solve the equation, $x^3 = 7x + 6$. Today we would put the equation in standard form and ask, "What are the zeros of $x^3 - 7x - 6 = 0$?" The related function is $y = x^3 - 7x - 6$.

**Step 1.** Graph the function, $y = x^3 - 7x - 6$ on your calculator. Note the zeros (the $x$-coordinates of the points where the graph intersects the $x$-axis). Clear your calculator.

**Step 2.** Al-Khayyami did not have a graphing calculator. He found the zeros of $y = x^3 - 7x - 6$ by using two second-degree curves given below. Their intersections provide the zeros of $y = x^3 - 7x - 6$. To see why this is true, try substituting the value for y, $y = -(\frac{1}{\sqrt{7}})x$, in $y^2 = x^2 + (\frac{6}{7})x$. You will get $x^3 = 7x + 6$.

With your calculator, you can quickly graph the 2 curves used by al-Khayyami:

1. $y_1 = -(\frac{1}{\sqrt{7}})x^2$, a parabola

2. $y_2^2 = x^2 + (\frac{6}{7})x$, a hyperbola.

Hint: Use both the positive and negative square roots of $x^2 + (\frac{6}{7})x$ to graph. Set your calculator "window" for $x$ min, −4.5; $x$ max, 4.5; $y$ max, 1; $y$ min, 4.

**Step 3.** Find the coordinates of the points of intersection of the graphs of $y_1$ and $y_2$. Are the values of the $x$-coordinates the same as the zeros you found for $y = x^3 - 7x - 6$?

*Algebra Activities from Many Cultures*

# Series: Number Patterns

## The Doubling Series

### MATERIALS

Reproducible 45

### ANSWERS

#### Story 1

1. Answers will vary; at 100 coins/dollar, $5,368,709.12

2. $2^{29}$ = 536,870,912 coins = $5,368,709.12

#### Story 2

1. Answers will vary.

2. $2^{21}$ cents = 2,097,152 cents, or $20,971.52

### EXTENSION ACTIVITY

Have students work in groups to develop their own stories about the surprising properties of the power series $2^n$.

## Egyptian Multiplication

### MATERIALS

Reproducible 46

### ANSWERS

1. Answers will vary.

2. 425    2448    1032

3.
| 1 | 85 |
|---|---|
| 10 | 850 |
| 20 | 1700 |
| 40 | 3400 |

4.
| 1 | 26 |
|---|---|
| 2 | 52 |
| 4 | 104 |
| 8 | 208 |
| 16 | 416 |
| 32 | 832 |

$832 + 104 + 52 + 26 = 1014$

$\dfrac{1014}{26} = 32 + 4 + 2 + 1 = 39$

## Base-2 Numerals in Ancient Egypt

### MATERIALS

Reproducible 47

### ANSWERS

1. Egyptian scribes: $12 = 8 + 4$
   Modern exponents: $12 = 2^3 + 2^2$
   Base-2 numeral: 1100

2. Egyptian scribes: $24 = 16 + 8$
   Modern exponents: $24 = 2^4 + 2^3$
   Base-2 numeral: 11000

3. Egyptian scribes: $39 = 32 + 4 + 2 + 1$
   Modern exponents:
   $39 = 2^5 + 2^2 + 2^1 + 2^0$
   Base-2 numerals: $39 = 100111$

## A Puzzle from Ancient Egypt

### MATERIALS

Reproducible 48

### PROCEDURE

1. Distribute the handout. If you wish, direct students to work in groups.

2. Students proceed as directed. Once they see that all three puzzles use multiples of 7, they should be able to fit the terms in the first column into a narrative.

## ANSWERS

1. Students should see that each number in the first column—other than the total—is 7 times the previous number.

2. Answers will vary.

## The Chinese Arithmetic Triangle

### MATERIALS

Reproducible 49

### ANSWERS

1. Successive rows have one additional term.

2. The sum is in the next row, under the space between the two terms.

## The Arithmetic Triangle in Africa, Asia, and Europe

### MATERIALS

Reproducible 50

### ANSWERS

1.

```
              1
            1   1
          1   2   1
        1   3   3   1
      1   4   6   4   1
    1   5  10  10   5   1
```

$(a + b)^6 =$ 1  6  15  20  15  6  1

## Series from India

### MATERIALS

Reproducible 51
paper and scissors or cuisenaire rods

### PROCEDURE

1. Divide the class into pairs or groups, if desired, and distribute the handouts.

2. Have students make a geometric model for the series given, using the Nilakantha method.

### ANSWERS

1. $5 \times 12 = 60$ units$^2$

2. The sum is 30, 1/2 of the area of the rectangle.

3. Students will make new model.

4. $S_n = n(a + l)/2$

## An Indian Series for $\pi$

### MATERIALS

Reproducible 52

### ANSWERS

1. Answers will vary.

2. Sum is getting closer to 0.7854.

3. Yes

4. No, $\pi/4$ is an irrational number.

# The Doubling Series

Egyptian mathematicians 4000 years ago were fascinated by the doubling series: 1, 2, 4, 8, 16, . . . which we now call the power series, $2^n$. Many people have developed amusing stories about the amazing properties of the doubling series. Here are two of these stories. You can fill in the happy (or unhappy) ending for each one.

## STORY 1: THE KING AND THE WISE MAN

A king wanted to reward his adviser, a wise man who had helped the king gain fame and fortune. So he asked the wise man to name his own reward. Did he want a palace, his best chariot, his daughter's hand in marriage? Name it and it would be his.

The wise man thanked the king but said he would ask only for some small coins each day for one month. The coins were to be counted out in a doubling pattern of one coin the first day, two coins the second day, four coins the third day, and so on for 30 days. The king thought this was too modest a request, but he had promised to grant the wise man's wish.

1. Without making any calculations, how do you think this story will end?

_____

2. If the coins were pennies, with 100 to the dollar, how much would the king have to pay on the 30th day?

_____

## STORY 2: THE FARMER AND THE HORSE TRADER

Years ago, a farmer wanted to buy a horse but the price was $160. "I don't have that much money," he said. The shrewd horse trader replied, "I'll give you the horse free of charge. Just buy the nails for his shoes. There are 6 nails in each shoe. Pay $\frac{1}{4}$ cent for the first, $\frac{1}{2}$, for the second, 1, 2, 4, and 8 cents for the remaining nails of that shoe, and so forth." The farmer jumped at the deal, expecting to pay about $10.

1. Without making any calculations, how do you think this story will end?

_____

2. If the coins were pennies, with 100 to the dollar, how much would the farmer have to pay for the last of the 24 nails needed?

_____

*Algebra Activities from Many Cultures*

# Egyptian Multiplication

Egyptian mathematicians 4000 years ago used the doubling series, $2^n$, to develop a convenient method of multiplication. Multiplication tables were not needed!

Example: $26 \times 13$

## Step 1

Arrange the numbers to be multiplied so that the smaller number is on the left. The product of $13 \times 26$ is the same as the product of $26 \times 13$, so changing the order of the numbers won't change the product.

$$13 \times 26$$

## Step 2

Set up two columns of numbers. The left column will always start with the number 1. Put the larger number of the problem in the column on the right.

$13 \times 26$

| | |
|---|---|
| 1 | 26 |

## Step 3

Double the number in each column, writing the sum in the next row of the column. Repeat this doubling process on both columns. Stop when the number in the **left** column would be **greater than** the smaller of the two numbers being multiplied.

$13 \times 26$

| | |
|---|---|
| 1 | 26 |
| 2 | 52 |
| 4 | 104 |
| 8 | 208 |

## Step 4

Find the numbers in the left column that **add up to** the smaller number being multiplied. In this case, $1 + 4 + 8 = 13$. Place a check mark beside each of these numbers. Then place a check beside each number in the same row of the right column.

$13 \times 26$

| | | | |
|---|---|---|---|
| ✓ | 1 | 26 | ✓ |
| | 2 | 52 | |
| ✓ | 4 | 104 | ✓ |
| ✓ | 8 | 208 | ✓ |

*(continued)*

*Algebra Activities from Many Cultures*

# Egyptian Multiplication *(continued)*

## Step 5

The numbers checked in the left column—1, 4, 8—are the multipliers of 26 whose sum adds up to 13. This means that the numbers checked in the right column—26, 104, 208—are partial products of $13 \times 26$. Since the sum of the multipliers is 13, the sum of the partial products will equal the product of $13 \times 26$. Add these partial products.

$$
\begin{array}{cc}
1 & 26 \\
+4 & 104 \\
\underline{\phantom{+}8} & \underline{208} \\
13 & 338 \\
\end{array}
$$

The product of $13 \times 26$ is 338.

Egyptian multiplication uses the same principles of algebra that we use today. Our modern method came from India, and was further improved by Islamic mathematicians of the Middle Ages. Check $13 \times 26$ the modern way:

$$
\begin{array}{r}
26 \\
\times 13 \\
\hline
78 \\
\underline{26\phantom{0}} \\
338 \\
\end{array}
$$

The modern method uses: $13 \times 26 = (3 + 10)\, 26 = 3(26) + 10\,(26)$.

The Egyptian method uses: $13 \times 26 = (1 + 4 + 8)\, 26 = 1(26) + 4\,(26) + 8\,(26)$.

The principle is the same: $(a + b)\, c = ac + bc$.

## Questions for Critical Thinking

1. An advantage of the Egyptian method is that the multiplication tables are not used and need not be memorized. Can you think of any disadvantages?

   _____

   _____

   _____

2. Do these multiplications the Egyptian way:

   $25 \times 17 =$ _____     $12 \times 204 =$ _____     $24 \times 43 =$ _____

*(continued)*

*Algebra Activities from Many Cultures*

# Egyptian Multiplication *(continued)*

3. For more rapid multiplication, the scribes would often multiply directly by 10, and then continue with doubling.

   **Example:** $20 \times 75 = 1500$

   | 1 | 75 |
   |---|---|
   | 10 | 750 |
   | 20 | 1500 |

   Follow the above example to multiply $40 \times 85$. First multiply by 10. Then double two times.

   Answer: _____

4. Divide 1014 by 26.

   Division problems were stated as the inverse of multiplication. To divide 1014 by 26, Egyptians would ask, "How many times must I multiply 26 to get 1014?"

   An Egyptian scribe would start with one 26, then double until there were partial products whose sum was 1014. Complete the example by doubling. Check the partial products that add up to 1014. Then check the multipliers in the same rows as those partial products. The sum of the multipliers is the same as the quotient of 1014/26.

   | ✓1 | 26 ✓ |
   |---|---|
   | ✓2 | 52 ✓ |
   | ____ | ____ |
   | ____ | ____ |
   | ____ | ____ |
   | ____ | ____ |

# Base-2 Numerals in Ancient Egypt

Egyptian multiplication works because whole-number multipliers can always be written as base-2 numbers. Modern computers also express numbers in base 2, using the digits 0 and 1. This is convenient because a computer consists largely of switches. An open switch has the value "0" and a closed switch has the value "1."

In Egyptian multiplication, the multiplier is expressed in base 2. On an earlier page, the multipliers 25, 12, 24, and 39 were used Let's look at those multipliers here in base-2 terms.

**Example.** Write the base-10 numeral 25 as a base-2 numeral. Start with 1 and double. Although Egyptians did not use exponents, they checked the powers of 2 that would add to 25.

✓ $1 = 2^0$ ✓

  $2 = 2^1$

  $4 = 2^2$

✓ $8 = 2^3$ ✓

✓ $16 = 2^4$ ✓

The sum of the checked numbers in the left-hand column—1, 8, 16—is 25. Therefore, the sum of the checked numbers in the right-hand column—$2^0, 2^3, 2^4$—is also 25. We can say that $25 = 1 + 8 + 16 = 2^0 + 2^3 + 2^4$.

**Three ways to express 25 as a power of 2:**

Egyptian scribes wrote:                      $25 = 16 + 8 + 1$

With modern exponents, we write:           $25 = 2^4 + 2^3 + 2^0$

Base-2 numeral with place value:           1 1 0 0 1

Here the zeros show that the positions for $2^1$ and $2^2$ are empty.

The 1 1 0 0 1 stands for $1 \times 2^4 + 1 \times 2^3 + 0 \times 2^2 + 0 \times 2^1 + 1 \times 2^0$, or  $\begin{matrix} 1 & 1 & 0 & 0 & 1 \\ 2^4 & 2^3 & 2^2 & 2^1 & 2^0 \end{matrix}$

**Express these base-10 numbers as powers of 2:**

1.  Egyptian scribes wrote:                    $12 = $ _____

    With modern exponents, we write:           $12 = $ _____

    Base-2 numeral with place value:           _____

2.  Egyptian scribes wrote:                    $24 = $ _____

    With modern exponents, we write:           $24 = $ _____

    Base-2 numeral with place value:           _____

3.  Egyptian scribes wrote:                    $39 = $ _____.

    With modern exponents, we write:           $39 = $ _____

    Base-2 numeral with place value:           _____

*Algebra Activities from Many Cultures*

# A Puzzle from Ancient Egypt

This puzzle was found in a mathematical papyrus written by the scribe Ah'mose almost 4000 years ago.

| | | House Inventory | |
|---:|---|---:|---:|
| 7 | houses | | |
| 49 | cats | | |
| 343 | mice | 1 | 2,801 |
| 2,401 | ears of grain | 2 | 5,602 |
| 16,807 | baskets of grain | 4 | 11,204 |
| 19,607 | Total | Total: 7 | 19,607 |

The first column appears to be the sum of a series. The second column shows 2801 multiplied by 7 for a product of 19,607. What does it mean?

The first column reminds us of the Mother Goose rhyme:

As I was going to St. Ives/
I met a man with seven wives/
Each wife had seven sacks/
Each sack had seven cats/
Each cat had seven kits/
Kits, cats, sacks and wives/
How many were going to St. Ives?

Of course, the answer is 1. Only the man was going to St. Ives!

About the year 1200, Leonard of Pisa, known as Fibonacci, returned from years of study in North Africa. He brought with him another puzzle that read:

Seven old women went to Rome. Each woman had seven mules; each mule carried seven sacks, each sack contained seven loaves; and with each loaf were seven knives; each knife was put up in seven sheaths.

1. Is there a connection among these three puzzles? If so, what is it?

_____

2. Make up a story for the Egyptian puzzle, starting with:

There was a man who had seven houses. In each house were seven cats . . .

97

*Algebra Activities from Many Cultures*

Name _____

Date _____

# The Chinese Arithmetic Triangle

Patterns of numbers or shapes provide clues for mathematics. If we understand the pattern, we can predict the next line, or the next value. Here is a pattern discovered in China, about 700 years ago, with a translation to modern numerals. This arithmetic triangle is widely used today in science and statistics. Many people do not know that the arithmetic triangle came from Asia and Africa because is has been renamed the "Pascal triangle." Blaise Pascal was a French mathematician who was born hundreds of years after the Chinese discovered the arithmetic triangle.

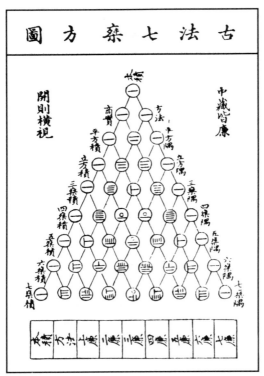

(after Needham)

```
                1
             1  2  1
          1  3  3  1
       1  4  6  4  1
    1  5  10 10  5  1
 1  6  15 20  15 6  1
```

Translation

## Questions for Critical Thinking

1. Study the number patterns in the Chinese arithmetic triangle. *Hint:* Count the number of terms in each row. What patterns can you find?

   _____

2. Add any two adjacent terms in a row. Can you find the sum in the triangle?

   _____

*Algebra Activities from Many Cultures*

# The Arithmetic Triangle in Africa, Asia, and Europe

## AFRICA

At the Science Academy in Cairo, Egypt, almost 1000 years ago, a great scientist was hard at work. His name was Ibn al-Haytham, and he was doing experiments with light. This work led to equations of higher degree. New methods were needed for their solution. One day he made an exciting discovery. When he multiplied $(a + b)^2$, $(a + b)^3$, $(a + b)^4$, $(a + b)^5$, and so on, the coefficients made a beautiful pattern. He described the pattern in a letter. But his beautiful pattern did not come down through the ages.

## ASIA

In Samarkand in Central Asia, also about 1000 years ago, Umar al-Khayyami was working on his book about algebra. He told friends that when he multiplied $(a + b)^2$, $(a + b)^3$, $(a + b)^4$, $(a + b)^5$, and so on, the coefficients made a beautiful pattern. But no copy of his pattern ever reached us. The same held true for another Islamic mathematician named al-Karaji, who worked in Baghdad. He put his diagram in a book he called *The Marvelous*, but the marvelous book vanished over the centuries.

In China, Jia Xian was also working on equations of higher degree. He made a triangle of the coefficients of $(a + b)^0$, $(a + b)^1$, $(a + b)^2$, $(a + b)^3$, $(a + b)^4$, $(a + b)^5$, and so on. In this case the triangle did survive. It was printed in a later book by Yang Hui, written in 1261 C.E. The diagram can also be found in another old Chinese book called *Precious Mirror of the Four Elements*. Many people call this diagram "the Chinese triangle."

## EUROPE

In France, Blaise Pascal (1623–1662) worked on higher-degree equations and published a copy of the triangle of coefficients of $(a + b)^n$. Europeans began to call the triangle "Pascal's triangle," although it was known hundreds of years earlier.

**Your triangle:** You can develop your own arithmetic triangle. Do the multiplications shown below but write only the coefficients in the lines.

$(a + b)^0 =$ ___

$(a + b)^1 =$ ___ ___

$(a + b)^2 =$ ___ ___ ___

$(a + b)^3 =$ ___ ___ ___ ___

$(a + b)^4 =$ ___ ___ ___ ___ ___

$(a + b)^5 =$ ___ ___ ___ ___ ___ ___

Can you predict, without multiplying the binomial, the terms of $(a + b)^6$?

*Algebra Activities from Many Cultures*

# Series from India

The Indian tradition in mathematics is thousands of years old, as old as India's civilization. Traders, builders, astronomers, and bookkeepers needed mathematics to carry out their business. To meet this need, Indian mathematicians developed the modern numerals and much of the arithmetic we use today. They also made important contributions to more advanced mathematics.

About 1500, the Indian mathematician Nilakantha make a geometric model for arithmetic series. An arithmetic series has a constant difference between any two successive terms. You can easily make a Nilakantha model for any arithmetic series. Use cuisenaire rods, or copy the diagram and cut out paper rectangles.

## PROJECT

Model the series: $2 + 4 + 6 + 8 + 10$

$a$ = first term, $l$ = last term, $d$ = the constant difference, $n$ = the number of terms, $S_n$ = the sum of the first $n$ terms of the series.

For this project, $a = 2$, $l = 10$, $d = 2$, $n = 5$, $S_5$ = Sum of the first five terms of the series.

Check off each step as you complete it.

❑ 1. Cut out five rectangles, or use cuisenaire rods. The rectangles should all be 1 unit high and with the following lengths: 2, 4, 6, 8, and 10. (These rectangles represent the terms of the series.)

❑ 2. Arrange the rectangles to look like a staircase, with the longest rectangle on the bottom, and the shortest rectangle on top.

❑ 3. Repeat steps 1 and 2. This will give you two "staircase" assemblies.

❑ 4. Move the bottom rectangle (for term of value 10) from one staircase assembly to abut the top rectangle of the other staircase. The lengthened top rectangle is now $2 + 10$ units long. Continue until you have fit all of the rectangles representing 8, 6, 4, and 2 onto the other staircase. It will make one large rectangle. The large rectangle represents two times the sum of the terms of the series you modeled.

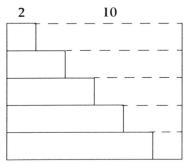

Nilakantha Model of 2 ( $2 + 4 + 6 + 8 + 10$ )

*(continued)*

© 1997 Beatrice Lumpkin
J. Weston Walch, Publisher

*Algebra Activities from Many Cultures*

# Series from India *(continued)*

## GROUP PROJECT AND DISCUSSION

1. What is the area of the large rectangle you formed?

   _____

2. Add terms of the series. Is the sum equal to the area of the large rectangle? Explain.

   _____

   _____

   _____

3. Using the method shown in the above example, make a geometric model for an arithmetic series of your choice. For each term, use cuisenaire rods or a rectangle cut out from paper. These small rectangles should have a width of 1 unit, and a length equal to the value of the term.

4. From the models you made above, derive the general formula for the sum of an arithmetic series of $n$ terms, whose first term is $a$, and whose last term is $l$.

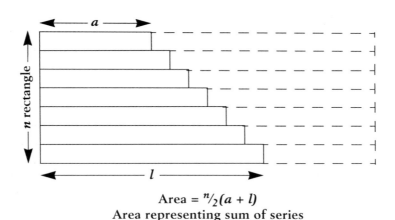

Area = $\frac{n}{2}(a + l)$
Area representing sum of series

$S_n =$ _____

# An Indian Series for π

The state of Kerala in Southwestern India was recently praised for its high level of education and health care. In the 1400's, Kerala was known for its high level of mathematics. Madhava of Sangamagramma, a mathematician who lived in Kerala, developed a series that we can use to evaluate π. In the West, it is named after Gregory (1667) although Madhava discovered the series hundreds of years earlier. The series is also important in the study of calculus.

For the case where $x = 1$ and the angle $\theta = 45°$, or $\pi/4$, the Madhava series becomes:

$$\pi/4 = 1 - \tfrac{1}{3} + \tfrac{1}{5} - \tfrac{1}{7} + \ldots$$

## Questions for Critical Thinking

1. Why do you think mathematicians think it so important to find accurate values for π?

2. Extend the series for $\pi/4$ for 10 additional terms. Fill in the following chart, rounding off to 4 decimal places. Is the sum getting closer or further from the value, $\pi/4 = 0.7854$?

| Term | 1 | $- \tfrac{1}{3}$ | $+ \tfrac{1}{5}$ | $- \tfrac{1}{7}$ |
|---|---|---|---|---|
| Sum | 1 | $\tfrac{2}{3}$ | .866 | .7238 |

| Term | 1 | $- \tfrac{1}{3}$ | $+ \tfrac{1}{5}$ | $- \tfrac{1}{7}$ | $+ \tfrac{1}{9}$ | $- \tfrac{1}{11}$ | $+ \tfrac{1}{13}$ | $- \tfrac{1}{15}$ | $+ \tfrac{1}{17}$ | $- \tfrac{1}{19}$ | $+ \tfrac{1}{21}$ | $- \tfrac{1}{23}$ | $+ \tfrac{1}{25}$ | $- \tfrac{1}{27}$ |
|---|---|---|---|---|---|---|---|---|---|---|---|---|---|---|
| Sum | 1 | $\tfrac{2}{3}$ | .866 | .7238 | .8349 | .7440 | .8209 | .7543 | .8131 | .7605 | .8081 | .7646 | .8046 | .7676 |

3. Could you extend the above series for $\pi/4$ indefinitely?

4. Do you think the series for $\pi/4$ would ever give you a "final" decimal value? Why or why not?

# Probability and Statistics

## Statistics from Ancient Egypt

### MATERIALS

Reproducible 53

### ANSWERS

1.

### Critical Thinking

2. No. Third difference would be zero.

3. 15 cubits: 747 arouras, 95, 6;
   16 cubits: 848 arouras, 101, 6

4. No. Floods above 17 cubits were destructive.

5.

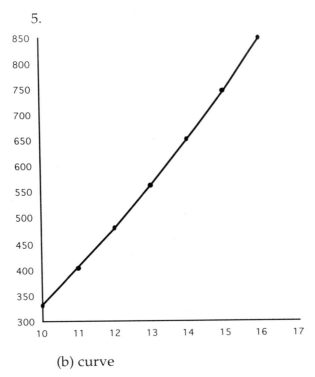

(b) curve

6. First difference must be constant for straight-line graphs.

## Rabbi Ibn Ezra's Formula

### MATERIALS

Reproducible 54

### ANSWERS

1. Answers will vary.

2. Answers will vary. Mathematics was enriched.

3. 175,560

4. 120

## Counting with Silk in Marrakesh

### MATERIALS

Reproducible 55
colored yarn
clear tape

### PROCEDURE

1. Divide the class into groups and distribute the handout.

2. Give students colored yarns to make models like those of Ibn Mun'im.

3. Have students proceed as directed on handout to make tree diagrams demonstrating permutations and combinations.

## Games of Chance: A Zuni Example

### MATERIALS

Reproducible 56
popsicle sticks (four for each student)
paints or markers for decorating sticks
basket or box to toss sticks into

### PROCEDURE

1. Divide the class into groups and distribute the handout.

2. Have students demonstrate the laws of probability by playing *tsaspatsawe*, keeping track of combinations of stick dice that appear with each toss.

3. After the game, discuss the *tsaspatsawe* scoring system, keeping in mind that scores aren't based on the probability of tossing a particular combination, but simply on the number of painted sides that show after each toss.

# Statistics from Ancient Egypt

The prosperity of ancient Egypt depended on water from the Nile River, which watered the fields when the river flooded once a year. If the flood was too low, some fields were left dry and barren. A flood that was too high, above 17 cubits, could wash away homes and destroy irrigation canals. To guard against famine, the government stored a supply of grain in case poor floods resulted in a poor harvest. Egyptians collected statistics on the height of the flood for thousands of years. By measuring the height of the annual flood, the government could calculate the size of the crops that could be expected.

Flood height was read on a scale called a Nilometer, marked off in *cubits*. A cubit length was about 0.525 m. Farm area was measured in *arouras*, each 10,000 cubits[2]. The following table lists the number of *arouras* of land watered for a selected length of river, for flood heights from 10 to 16 cubits. This table has a hidden pattern that can be found by using the method of differences.

## Questions for Critical Thinking

1. Study the patterns in this table.

| Flood Height and Area Watered | | | |
|---|---|---|---|
| Flood height in cubits | *Arouras* of land watered | 1st difference | 2nd difference |
| 10 | 332 | | |
| 11 | 403 | 71 | |
| 12 | 480 | 77 | 6 |
| 13 | 563 | 83 | 6 |
| 14 | 652 | 89 | |
| 15 | | | |
| 16 | | | |

*(continued)*

*Algebra Activities from Many Cultures*

# Statistics from Ancient Egypt *(continued)*

2. Can you take a third difference in this table? Why or why not?

   _____

   _____

   _____

   _____

3. Assuming that the pattern in the table continues, complete the table on the previous page for flood heights of 15 cubits and 16 cubits.

4. Would it make sense to extend the table to 17 cubits, 18 cubits and more? Why or why not?

   _____

   _____

   _____

   _____

5. On a sheet of graph paper, label the *x*-axis "Flood height in cubits." Label the *y*-axis, "Area of land watered in arouras." Plot points on this graph, using the values for Flood Height and Area Watered in the chart that you completed above.

   (a) Connect the points with a smooth graph.

   (b) Is the graph that you just plotted a straight line or a curve? _____

6. How could you have predicted the answer to question 5 from the table of differences?

   _____

   _____

   _____

   _____

# Rabbi Ibn Ezra's Formula

By the year 1100, mathematicians in India and the Islamic countries were finding sophisticated ways to count. The motivation was the age-old desire to control the powers of nature, in this case through magic and the study of astrology. An unknown Jewish author of the *Sefer Yetsirah* *(Book of Creation)* asked, "How many ways can the 22 letters of the Hebrew alphabet be arranged, taken 2 at a time, 3 at a time, 4 at a time, etc.?" It was thought that some arrangements of letters produced formulas with magical powers. The author discovered the rule we use today, that the number of possible arrangements of *n* letters was *n*.

Astrology was also the motivation for work by Rabbi Abraham ben Meir ibn Ezra (1090–1167). He was a Spanish Jewish scholar who worked in Islamic Spain. Islamic mathematicians of that period included Jews and Christians as well as Muslims. As an astrologer, ibn Ezra believed that people's fates were controlled by the conjunction of the planets. He calculated the number of possible combinations of 7 heavenly bodies, including the sun, moon, Mars, Jupiter, Saturn, Venus, and Mercury. Most feared was the conjunction of all 7 bodies. In that time they were all called "planets" but now we know that the sun is a star and the moon is a satellite of Earth.

For the simplest case, taking 2 "planets" at a time out of 7, ibn Ezra found the number was 21. He continued his calculation for combinations taking 3 at a time, then 4 at a time. His work showed an understanding of our modern formula for combinations of *n* objects taken *r* at a time.

$$C_r^n = \frac{n!}{r!(n-r)!}$$

## Questions for Critical Thinking

1. Do you believe in lucky numbers? Why or why not? _____

   _____

2. History has not recorded any success in the search for "magic" Hebrew words or any other "magic" words. Do you think this search was a waste of time?

   _____

   _____

3. How many 4-letter arrangements are there of the 22 letters of the Hebrew alphabet if no letters are repeated?

   _____

4. With 7 "planets" how many possible conjunctions are there? Hint:  Include conjunctions of 2, 3, 4, 5, 6, and 7 planets.

   _____

# Counting with Silk in Marrakesh

Ahmad Ibn Mun'im was a great mathematician of the thirteenth century. He developed basic formulas for permutations and combinations. Hundreds of years would pass before these principles became known to European mathematicians. Born in Spain, near Valencia, Ibn Mun'im moved to North Africa where he earned his living as a physician. Many mathematicians of that time practiced medicine to earn a living. They did their mathematics research in their spare time.

Most of Ibn Mun'im's work was done in Marrakesh, a city of gardens located in the Atlas mountains of Morocco. Marrakesh was a center of the silk industry. That may explain why Ibn Mun'im chose silk threads of different colors to demonstrate the principles of permutations and combinations. He was a great teacher and gave his students more than one way to learn mathematics.

One way was to look at the arithmetic triangle. Notice that it was not called the Pascal triangle because that was 400 years before Pascal was born. To understand Ibn Mun'im's method, compare the number of combinations that can be selected from four objects (zero object, one object, two objects, three objects, four objects) with the fourth row of the arithmetic triangle.

$$\begin{array}{ccccccccc}
 & & & & 1 & & & & \\
 & & & 1 & & 2 & & 1 & \\
 & & 1 & & 3 & & 3 & & 1 \\
 & 1 & & 4 & & 6 & & 4 & & 1
\end{array}$$

**1          4     6     4          1**   4th row of the arithmetic triangle

**Arithmetic Triangle**

$$\binom{4}{0} = 1, \quad \binom{4}{1} = 4, \quad \binom{4}{2} = 6, \quad \binom{4}{3} = 4, \quad \binom{4}{4} = 1$$

A physical model using red, blue, green, and yellow silk threads was another way Ibn Mun'im showed combinations of 4 objects. For example, for $\binom{4}{3}$, he modeled:

| Red | Red | Red | Blue |
|------|--------|--------|--------|
| Blue | Blue | Green | Green |
| Green | Yellow | Yellow | Yellow |

## GROUP PROJECT

1. For $\binom{5}{r}$, $r = 0, 1, 2, 3, 4, 5$, make models like those of Ibn Mun'im, using colored yarns. Members of the group can divide the work, each modeling one or two of the combinations. Clear tape can be used to attach the yarn to a display board.

2. Make a tree diagram with colored yarns to show how many permutations are possible for 4 things, arranged 4 at a time.

*Algebra Activities from Many Cultures*

# Games of Chance:  A Zuni Example

People began to study the laws of probability long before the beginning of written mathematics. Although all cultures feature games of skill, people have also enjoyed games of chance. Scoring systems in games of chance have developed over a period of time. For people to enjoy a game of chance, they must believe that the scoring system is fair.

The Zuni are a Native American "pueblo" people who have developed a high civilization. They have borrowed a game from their neighbors, the Dine (Navajo), that you can enjoy. It is called *tsaspatsawe*. You can make stick dice for the game of *tsaspatsawe* from 4 popsicle sticks, colored and decorated on one side. Sticks are tossed in a basket. The method of scoring is simple. The number of points for a toss is the number of painted sides that show. The game ends when a player gets 10 points, or whatever number of points the players have decided wins the game.

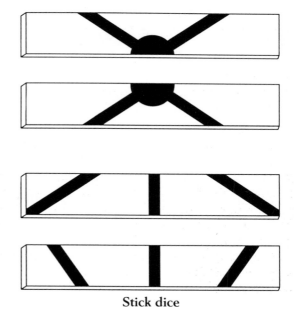

Stick dice

## TSASPATSAWE

## Group Project

**Goal:** To demonstrate laws of probability using Zuni stick dice. Check off each step as you complete it.

❑ 1. For each group member, prepare 4 popsicle (or heavier stock) stick dice, leaving one side plain and coloring the other side as illustrated above.

❑ 2. Identify the sticks with a number, 1 to 4. Pencil the number on each side of the stick. These numerals do not affect the game but help in the scientific analysis of the game.

❑ 3. Play a few games of *tsaspatsawe* to see how it works.

## Experiment

❑ 4. In a basket or box, make 96 tosses of the 4 stick dice, recording the results of each toss. Students can each do a number of tosses, or work as partners with a tosser and recorder taking turns. Using C for colored, or U for uncolored, make a list of the results. A table makes it easier to tally results for sticks 1, 2, 3, and 4. Fill in the rest of the table and begin your tosses.

*(continued)*

## Games of Chance:  A Zuni Example *(continued)*

**Stick**

|   |   |   |   |   |   |   |   |   |   |   |   |   |   |   |   |   |
|---|---|---|---|---|---|---|---|---|---|---|---|---|---|---|---|---|
| 1 | C | C | C | C | C | C | C | C | U | U | U | U | U | U | U | U |
| 2 | C | C | C | C | U | U | U | U | C |
| 3 | C | C | U | U | U | C | C | U | C |
| 4 | C | U | U | C | U | C | U | C | C |

**tally**

❑ 5. Tally the results of your 96 tosses. Then combine your results according to the Zuni scoring system. For example, CCUU will give the same score as CUCU, CUUC, UUCC, UCUC, and UCCU. Do you find 1 way to get 4 colored sides up, 6 ways to get 2, 4 ways to get 3, 4 ways to get 1, and only 1 way to get 0 colored sides up?

Number of tosses with

4 colored sides up _____

3 colored sides up _____

2 colored sides up _____

1 colored side up _____

0 colored sides up _____

## Group Discussion

Is tsaspatsawe a fair game? Why or why not?

_____

_____

_____

Would you want to change the scoring system?

_____

_____

*Algebra Activities from Many Cultures*

# Problem Solving

## Benjamin Banneker: Puzzle Solver

### MATERIALS

Reproducible 57

### ANSWERS

1. 9.6

2. Ages in years, 32, 64, 81

3. 864

## Kill No Camels

### MATERIALS

Reproducible 58

### ANSWERS

1. Answers will vary.

2. No; $\frac{1}{2} + \frac{1}{3} + \frac{1}{9} = \frac{17}{18}$, less than the whole.

3. Answers will vary.

## Problem Solving in India: Inverse Operations

### MATERIALS

Reproducible 59

## ANSWERS

| Operation Given | Inverse Operation | Result |
|---|---|---|
| Final result, 4 | Start with 4 | 4 |
| Divide by 8 | Multiply by 8 | 32 |
| Add 10 | Subtract 10 | 22 |
| Extract square root | Square the number | 484 |
| Diminish by 92 | Add 92 | 576 |
| Multiply by itself | Take square root | 24 |
| Diminish by $\frac{1}{3}$ (or multiply by $\frac{2}{3}$) | Increase by $\frac{1}{2}$ (or multiply by $\frac{3}{2}$) | 36 |
| Divide by 7 | Multiply by 7 | 252 |
| Increase by $\frac{1}{2}$ | Diminish by $\frac{1}{3}$ | 168 |
| Multiply by 4 | Divide by 4 | 42 = answer |

## Problems Solving in Latin America

### MATERIALS

Reproducible 60

### ANSWERS

1. $3x^2 = 1875$; 75 in front and 25 deep

2. $3x^2 + 12x = 420$; $x = 10, -14$; solution pairs are (10, 30) and (−14, −42)

3. 60 varas, 90 varas

4. $729a^4 = 944784$; numbers are 6, 18, 54, 162

5. $60 + 1$

6. Diez was correct.

# Benjamin Banneker:
# Puzzle Solver

Benjamin Banneker became famous as the "African astronomer," who published calculations for eclipses in his almanac for 1792. He is remembered for his work in the survey that planned the nation's capital. Few realize that he was already past middle age before he had his first chance to see a book on astronomy. But Banneker had kept his mind sharp by solving mathematical puzzles. At age 57, once he got the books and a telescope, he was able to teach himself astronomy and trigonometry. The following puzzles are adapted from Banneker's *Manuscript Journal*.

## Questions for Critical Thinking

1. Divide 60 into four parts, that the first being increased by 4, the second decreased by 4, the third multiplied by 4, the fourth part divided by 4, that the sum, the difference, the product and the quotient shall be one and the same number. Find the number. *Hint:* Work backwards. Let your unknown be the "one and the same number."

2. Banneker wrote that 3 people were talking about their ages:

    "Says A, if from double the cube root of B's age, double the 4th root of C's age be taken, the remainder will be equal to the 5th Root of my age.
    Says B, the square root of my age is equal to $\frac{1}{4}$ of A's.
    Says C, the square root of my age is 1 more than the square root of B's.
    Required their several Ages—"

    *Hint:* Assume ages are in whole years and try reasonable values for A's age.

3. Banneker wrote a poem puzzle about a dog running to catch a rabbit. The distances are given in terms of the dog's leaps. The rabbit had a head start equal to 30 dog leaps and leaped 4 times in the time it took the dog to make 3 leaps. But the rabbit had to leap 3 times to equal the distance that the dog covered in 2 leaps.

    Just as the dog was about to catch the rabbit, the rabbit turned instantly. It took the dog a time equal to 3 dog leaps to make the turn. Assume that the rabbit made 22 turns. How many leaps did it take for the dog to catch the rabbit?

*Algebra Activities from Many Cultures*

# Kill No Camels

Here is a puzzle that's traveled around the world. Some of the world's best mathematics was developed in Medieval Islam to handle complicated inheritance laws. This puzzle made its way from across Asia and North Africa, into Spain and into Cuba, where it appeared in a high school mathematics book. It has even been adopted by the Harvard Business School as an example of the benefit of negotiation. Here is Harvard University 1990's version.

An old man dies and leaves an inheritance of 17 camels to his three children. His instructions are to give $\frac{1}{2}$ to the eldest, $\frac{1}{3}$ to the middle child, and $\frac{1}{9}$ to the youngest. However, no camels are to be slaughtered.

Well, the three heirs were puzzled. Then they began to argue. Then they began to cry, because their father was dead and they were arguing among themselves. So they decided to stop the argument and get some advice from a wise old woman who was their neighbor.

The old woman listened quietly. Then she went out to her yard, got her own camel, and said, "Take my camel. It will help you make a fair division."

The heirs took her camel. Added to the inheritance of 17 camels, they now had 18 to divide. The eldest took $\frac{1}{2}$ of 18, or 9. The middle child took $\frac{1}{3}$ of 18, or 6. The youngest took $\frac{1}{9}$ of 18, or 2. That left 1 camel which they returned, with thanks, to their neighbor. The happy ending to this story shows the benefit of negotiating, rather than fighting it out.

## Questions for Critical Thinking

1. Why do you think the father left that type of will?

   _____

2. Ordinarily, would shares of $\frac{1}{2}$, $\frac{1}{3}$, and $\frac{1}{9}$ distribute an entire inheritance? Explain.

   _____

3. Can you think of other solutions that might be acceptable?

   _____

*Algebra Activities from Many Cultures*

# Problem Solving in India: Inverse Operations

Mathematics was developed to solve problems of real life. We can learn much from the problem solving methods from our multicultural heritage. A good example is the method of inversion from India, described by Aryabhata.

When he was only 23 years old, Aryabhata wrote an important book on astronomy and mathematics. That was about 1500 years ago but we still find his work fascinating. When India's first satellite was launched in 1975 in the former Soviet Union, it was named "Aryabhata" after him. In Aryabhata's time, c. 500, the method of working backwards from the final result was used to solve problems. The Indians called the method "inversion." To a woman who studied mathematics in India at that time, Aryabhata put this challenge:

O beautiful maiden with beaming eyes, tell me, since you understand the method of inversion:

What number multiplied by 3, then increased by $\frac{3}{4}$ of the product, then divided by 7, then diminished by $\frac{1}{3}$ of the result, then multiplied by itself, then diminished by 52, whose square root is then extracted before 8 is added, and then divided by 10, gives the final result of 2?

The method was to start at the end and to do the inverse operations:

| Operation given | Inverse operation | Result |
| --- | --- | --- |
| Final result, 2 | Start with 2 | 2 |
| Divide by 10 | Multiply by 10 | 20 |
| Add 8 | Subtract 8 | 12 |
| Extract square root | Square the number | 144 |
| Diminish by 52 | Add 52 | 196 |
| Multiply by itself | Take square root | 14 |
| Diminish by $\frac{1}{3}$ (multiply by $\frac{2}{3}$) | Increase by $\frac{1}{2}$ (multiply by $\frac{3}{2}$) | 21 |
| Divide by 7 | Multiply by 7 | 147 |
| Add $\frac{3}{4}$ product (multiply by $\frac{7}{4}$) | Multiply product by $\frac{4}{7}$ | 84 |
| Multiply by 3 | Divide by 3 | 28 |

The desired number is 28.

*(continued)*

*Algebra Activities from Many Cultures*

Name _____

Date _____

# Problem Solving in India:  Inverse Operations (continued)

It takes a moment's thought to realize that the inverse of "diminish by $\frac{1}{3}$" is to increase by $\frac{1}{2}$. Another way to look at it is that to subtract $\frac{1}{3}$ of the quantity from the quantity is the same as multiplying by $\frac{2}{3}$. The inverse of multiplying by $\frac{2}{3}$ is to multiply by $\frac{3}{2}$. Also, "add $\frac{3}{4}$ of a number" is the same as multiplying the number by $\frac{7}{4}$. The inverse operation is to multiply the number by $\frac{4}{7}$.

**Directions:** Work "backwards" to solve the following puzzle. Start with the final step and use the inverse operations until you find the unknown number.

## Inverse Operations

What number multiplied by 4, then increased by $\frac{1}{2}$ of the product, then divided by 7, then diminished by $\frac{1}{3}$ of the result, then multiplied by itself, then diminished by 92, whose square root is then extracted before 10 is added, and then divided by 8, gives the final result of 4?

| Operation given | Inverse operation | Result |
|---|---|---|
| Final result, 4 | | |
| Divide by 8 | | |
| 10 is added | | |
| Extract square root | | |
| Diminish by 92 | | |
| Multiply by itself | | |
| Diminish by $\frac{1}{3}$ | | |
| (multiply by $\frac{2}{3}$) | | |
| Divide by 7 | | |
| Increase by $\frac{1}{2}$ | | |
| Multiply by 4 | | |

*Algebra Activities from Many Cultures*

# Problems Solving in
# Latin America

The first five of the following examples come from a book, written in 1732 by Juan Joseph de Padilla of Guatemala. The sixth, by Juan Diez, was published in Mexico in 1553.

**Directions:** Solve and check your solutions.

1. A squadron of 1875 soldiers are lined up, forming a rectangle that is 3 times longer in front than on the sides. How many are standing across the front, and how many rows deep is the array? (Note that European armies used to fight in rectangular arrays.)

    _____

2. Find two numbers, given that the second is triple the first. If you multiply the first by the second, and the second by 4, the sum of the products is 420. De Padilla found only one pair of answers. Can you find two pairs?

    _____

3. A length of wood sold for 2 *reales* per *vara*. Another length of wood 30 *varas* longer sold at 4 *reales* per *vara*. If the longer wood brought in a price 3 times the price of the shorter wood, how long was each piece of wood? (A *vara* was 0.83 meters.)

    _____

4. For a geometric series with constant multiplier 3, find 4 terms whose product equals 944,784.
    (*Hint:* In a geometric series with first term $a$, and with 3 as the constant multiplier, the terms are: $a, 3a, 9a, 27a, \ldots$)

    _____

5. Find a number which divided by 2, 3, 4, 5, or 6 always has a remainder of 1.
    (*Hint:* Find a number divisible by 2, 3, 4, 5 or 6, and add 1.)

    _____

6. Select five weights that can be combined to weigh any integral amount from 1 to 120 *tomines*. Weights can be used in either pan of a balance. (*Tomine* is Arabic for *eight*. Eight *tomines* exchanged for one *real*.) Diez gives the answer as 1, 3, 9, 27, and 81 *tomines*. Do you agree?

    _____

# Bibliography

Arnold, Dieter. *Building in Egypt*. New York: Oxford University Press, 1991.

Ascher, Marcia. *Ethnomathematics*. New York: Brooks Cole, 1991.

Ascher, Maria, and Robert Ascher. *Code of the Quipu*. Ann Arbor, MI: University of Michigan, 1981.

Berggren, J.L. *Episodes in the Mathematics of Medieval Islam*. New York: Springer Verlag, 1980.

Bunt, L., P. Jones, and J. Bedient. *The Historical Roots of Elementary Mathematics*. Englewood Cliffs, NJ: Prentice Hall, 1976.

Chace, Arnold B. *The Rhind Mathematical Papyrus*. Reston, VA: NCTM, 1979. Translation of ancient Egyptian mathematics text, c. 1800 BCE.

Chicago Public Schools. *Algebra I Framework*. 1991. Ten units, each with at least one multicultural situation and examples.

Closs, Michael P., ed. *Native American Mathematics*. Austin, TX: University of Texas, 1988. Includes chapters on Latino heritage; quipu from Peru, and Maya and Aztec numerals.

Gerdes, Paulus. *Lusona, Geometrical Recreations of Africa*. Maputo, Mozambique: Eduardo Mondlane University, 1991. Available from Arthur B. Powell, Academic Foundations, Rutgers University, Newark, NJ 07102.

Gillings, Richard J. *Mathematics in the Time of the Pharoahs*. Cambridge, MA: Harvard University Press, 1975.

Joseph, George Gheverghese. *The Crest of the Peacock—Non-European Roots of Mathematics*. London: Taurus, 1991. Indian and Chinese mathematics.

Katz, Victor. *A History of Mathematics*. New York: Harper Collins, 1993. Many multicultural examples.

Kenschaft, Patricia, C. "Black Women in Mathematics in the United States," *The American Mathematical Monthly*, vol. 88, no. 8, October 1981. "Black Men and Women in Mathematical Research," *Journal of Black Studies*. December 1987, 170–190.

Lumpkin, Beatrice. "From Egypt to Benjamin Banneker: African Origins of False Position Solutions," *Vita Mathematica, Historical Research and Integration with Teaching*. Ronald Callinger, ed. Washington, DC: Mathematics Association of America, 1996, 279–289.

Lumpkin, Beatrice, and Dorothy Strong. *Multicultural Connections, Science and Mathematics Activities and Projects*. Portland, ME: J. Weston Walch, Publisher, 1995.

Lumpkin, Beatrice, and Arthur B. Powell. *Math—A Rich Heritage*. Upper Saddle River, NJ: Globe Fearon, 1995.

———. *Multiculturalism in Mathematics, Science and Technology*. Menlo Park, NJ: Addison-Wesley, 1992.

Robins, Gay, and Charles Shute. *The Rhind Mathematical Papyrus—an ancient Egyptian text*. New York: Dover, 1987.

Van Sertima, Ivan, ed. *Blacks in Science*, Journal of African Civilizations. New Brunswick, NJ: Transaction Books, 1983.

Yan, Li and Du Shiran. *Chinese Mathematics—A Concise History*. tr. John N. Crossley, and Anthony W.C. Lun. Oxford: Clarendon, 1987.

Zaslavsky, Claudia. *Africa Counts*. Westport, CT: Lawrence Hill, 1979.

———. *Multicultural Mathematics*. Portland, ME: J. Weston Walch, Publisher, 1993.

———. *Fear of Math*. New Brunswick, NJ: Rutgers University Press, 1994.

———. *The Multicultural Classroom*. Portsmouth, NH: Heinemann, 1995.

# Index

# Share Your Bright Ideas with Us!

**We want to hear from you! Your valuable comments and suggestions will help us meet your current and future classroom needs.**

Your name_____Date_____

School name_____Phone_____

School address_____

Grade level taught_____Subject area(s) taught_____Average class size_____

Where did you purchase this publication?_____

Was your salesperson knowledgeable about this product?   Yes_____   No_____

What monies were used to purchase this product?

___School supplemental budget        ___Federal/state funding        ___Personal

**Please "grade" this Walch publication according to the following criteria:**

Quality of service you received when purchasing ....................................................A   B   C   D   F

Ease of use............................................................................................................A   B   C   D   F

Quality of content.................................................................................................A   B   C   D   F

Page layout ..........................................................................................................A   B   C   D   F

Organization of material .......................................................................................A   B   C   D   F

Suitability for grade level.......................................................................................A   B   C   D   F

Instructional value................................................................................................A   B   C   D   F

COMMENTS:_____

_____

What specific supplemental materials would help you meet your current—or future—instructional needs?

_____

Have you used other Walch publications? If so, which ones?_____

May we use your comments in upcoming communications?      ___Yes      ___No

Please **FAX** this completed form to **207-772-3105**, or mail it to:

   **Product Development,  J.Weston Walch, Publisher, P.O. Box 658, Portland, ME 04104-0658**

We will send you a **FREE GIFT** as our way of thanking you for your feedback.   **THANK YOU!**